ELEC

Other Titles of Interest

160   Coil Design and Construction Manual

BP53   Practical Electronics Calculations and Formulae

BP144   Further Practical Electronics Calculations and Formulae

BP286   A Reference Guide to Basic Electronics Terms

BP287   A Reference Guide to Practical Electronics Terms

BP316   Practical Electronic Design Data

BP401   Transistor Data Tables

ELECTRONIC HOBBYISTS
DATA BOOK

by

R. A. Penfold

BERNARD BABANI (publishing) LTD
THE GRAMPIANS
SHEPHERDS BUSH ROAD
LONDON W6 7NF
ENGLAND

Please Note

Although every care has been taken with the production of this book to ensure that any projects, designs, modifications and/or programs, etc., contained herewith, operate in a correct and safe manner and also that any components specified are normally available in Great Britain, the Publishers do not accept responsibility in any way for the failure, including fault in design, of any project, design, modification or program to work correctly or to cause damage to any other equipment that it may be connected to or used in conjunction with, or in respect of any other damage or injury that may be so caused, nor do the Publishers accept responsibility in any way for the failure to obtain specified components.

Notice is also given that if equipment that is still under warranty is modified in any way or used or connected with home-built equipment then that warranty may be void.

First Published – March 1996

British Library Cataloguing in Publication Data
Penfold, R. A.
  Electronic Hobbyists Data Book
  I. Title
  537.5

  ISBN 0 85934 396 0

Printed and bound in Great Britain by Cox & Wyman Ltd, Reading

Preface

The hobby of electronics can be a bewildering one at times. There seems to be an ever increasing range of electronic components and circuit configurations for them to operate in. A mass of data is associated with these components and circuits, ranging from the mundane such as resistor colour codes, to more specialised data such as performance figures for specialist integrated circuits. Most electronics hobbyists accumulate a large amount of data from sources such as books, magazines, and electronic component catalogues. This brings the problem of locating each piece of data that is required, if it is actually present in the collection.

The aim of this book is to provide a large collection of data for the amateur electronics enthusiast, so that much of the information he or she will require is available in a single source where it can be quickly and easily located. It would obviously be unrealistic to claim that this book contains all the data that will ever be required by the average electronics enthusiast. However, it contains a wide range of data covering subjects such as common circuits, MIDI, computing, radio, colour codes, logic integrated circuits, operational amplifiers, transistors, and other types of semiconductor. The aim of the book is not to provide a course in electronics, and some background knowledge of the subject is needed in order to fully utilize this publication. In most cases the reader is not simply presented with raw data though, and most of the data is backed up by explanatory notes.

R. A. Penfold

Contents

Page

Chapter 1 – CIRCUIT DATA 1
  L–C Tuned Circuits 1
  Meter Resistors 4
  Digital Meters 6
  L.E.D. Current 8
  555 Monostable 9
  CMOS Monostables 14
  555 Astable 19
  Wien Oscillator 23
  Basic C – R Filters 27
  Twin T Filter 30
  Bandpass Filter 35
  State Variable Filter 36
  Power Supplies 37
  Rectifiers 43
  Smoothing Capacitor 46
  Voltage Regulators 48
  Variable Voltage 51
  Zeners 53
  Current Regulators 58

Chapter 2 – CODES, ETC. 63
  Resistor Codes 63
  Five Band Codes 65
  Old Codes 68
  Potentiometers 70
  Inductors 70
  Capacitors 70
  Tantalum Bead 72
  Ceramic Capacitors 73
  Other Codes 73
  Preferred Values 75

Chapter 3 – OPERATIONAL AMPLIFIERS 77
  Inverting Mode 77
  Gain-Bandwidth 79
  Non-Inverting Mode 81
  Compensation 83
  Offset Null 86

Chapter 3 (Continued   **Page**

Audio Amplification 88
Terminology 90
Offset Voltage 90
Slew Rate 90
Large Signal Bandwidth 91
Common Mode Rejection 91
Latch-Up 91
Output Voltage Swing 92
Output Resistance 92
Real Devices 92
Pseudo Op. Amps 98

Chapter 4 – LOGIC ICs 101
Standard TTL 102
Low Power 103
LS TTL 104
The Rest 105
CMOS 106
Micro Power 107
High Speed CMOS 110
Which TTL? 111
CMOS 122
Gates 143
Inverter Truth Table 143
2 Input AND Gate Truth Table 145
2 Input OR Gate Truth Table 145
4 Input AND Gate Truth Table 145
2 Input NAND Gate Truth Table 146
2 Input NOR Gate Truth Table 146
4 Input NAND Gate Truth Table 147
2 Input XOR Gate Truth Table 148
2 Input XNOR Gate Truth Table 148
3 Input XOR Gate Truth Table 148

Chapter 5 – TRANSISTORS, ETC. 149
Parameters 150
    h_{FE} 150
    h_{fe} 151
    V_{CBO} 151
    V_{CEO} 151
    T_j 151

Chapter 5 (Continued)   **Page**

    P_{tot} 152
    V_{EBO} 152
    I_C 153
    f_T 153
    I_{CBO} 154
    $V_{CE(sat)}$ 154
    t_{ON} 154
    t_{OFF} 155
Amplifying Modes 155
Common Base 157
Emitter Follower 158
Darlington Pair 160
Type Numbers 161
Gain Groups 162
JEDEC Codes 163
JIS Codes 164
Manufacturers Digits 165
Tables 166
  Transistor Characteristic Tables:
  Small–medium Power Audio Transistors 166
  Small–medium Power R.F. Transistors 168
  Power Transistors 169
FETs 170
FET Parameters 175
    f_T 175
    P_{TOT} 176
    V_p 176
    V_{GGS} 176
    V_{DG} 176
    V_{DS} 176
    C_{iss} 176
    g_m 176
    $V_{GS(th)}$ 177
    I_{DSS} 177
    I_{GSS} 177
    I_D 177
    I_{Dss} 177
    t_{on} 178
    t_{off} 178
    R_{DS} 178

Chapter 5 (Continued)   **Page**

   $V_{DS(on)}$ 178
  FET Characteristics 179
   Small Signal FETs 179
   Power MOSFETs 179
  Unijunctions 180
   V_{BB} 181
   I_P 182
   I_V 184
   I_E 184
   P_{TOT} 184
   R_{BB} 184
   n 184
  Diodes 185
  Parameters 186
   PIV 187
   I_f 187
   I_R 188
   $V_{F\,Drop}$ 188
   T_{rr} 188
   T_j 188
  SCRs 189
   V_r 190
   V_f 190
   I_f 190
   V_g 190
   I_g 190
   I_{hm} 190
   V_{fm} 191
  Triacs and Diacs 192

Chapter 6 – MISCELLANEOUS DATA 195
  Short Wave Bands 195
  Short Wave Broadcast Bands 195
  Short Wave Amateur Band 195
  CB Frequency Allocations 196
  Frequency–Wavelength Conversion 199
  Amateur Abbreviations 200
  Q Codes 203
  SINPO 204
  Signal Strength 204

Chapter 6 (Continued)

Interference 205
Noise 205
Propagation Disturbance 205
Overall Rating 205
Baudot Codes 205
Morse Code 207
ASCII Codes 208
MIDI Codes 212
MIDI Instructions and Codes 214
Note On/Off 214
Key Pressure 215
Control Change, Etc. 215
Pitch Wheel 216
Programme Change 216
System Messages 217
General MIDI 219
General MIDI Sound Assignment Groups 221
Melodic Instrument Sound Assignments 221
Circuit Symbols 225
Centronics Interface 230
RS232C 234
Parallel R – Series C 236
Amplifier Output Power 238
Peak – R.M.S. 238
Decibel Ratios 239

Chapter 1

CIRCUIT DATA

This chapter covers basic design data for a range of common circuit types. These include 555 astable and monostable circuits, meter series and shunt resistances, series and parallel tuned circuits, etc. In addition to basic design formulae, a number of useful tables and graphs are provided. Note that basic operational amplifier circuits and transistor amplifier circuits are covered in separate chapters dealing with operational amplifiers and transistors.

L-C Tuned Circuits

There are two types of simple $L - C$ tuned circuit, which are the parallel and series varieties. These are shown in Figures 1.1(a) and 1.1(b) respectively. When added into the signal path a parallel tuned circuit provides a low impedance at most frequencies, but a high impedance at or close to the resonant frequency. In theory at any rate, there is infinite impedance through a parallel tuned circuit at the resonant frequency. When used in the manner shown in Figure 1.1(a) a parallel tuned circuit therefore provides a notch response. This type of circuit is sometimes referred to as a "wavetrap". A parallel tuned circuit is more frequently used in the manner shown in Figure 1.2, where it provides a bandpass response. In practice the tuned circuit is often used as the load for an amplifier, rather than in the manner shown in Figure 1.2. The result is still a bandpass response. A series tuned circuit has a high impedance at most frequencies, but a low impedance close to resonance. Series resonant tuned circuits are little used in practice. In both cases the resonant frequency is given by the formula:-

$$f = 1/2\pi \sqrt{LC}$$

These tables shows the approximate resonant frequencies for some example $L - C$ values.

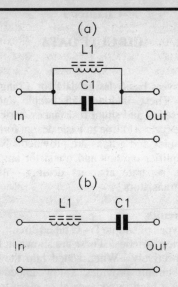

Fig.1.1   (a) Parallel resonant and (b) series resonant tuned circuits

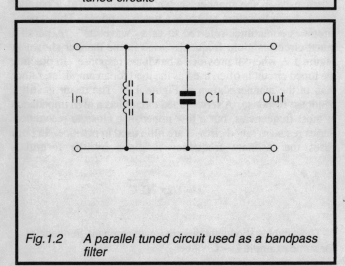

Fig.1.2   A parallel tuned circuit used as a bandpass filter

Inductance	5p	10p	20p	40p	100p
0.1μH	225MHz	159MHz	112MHz	79.6MHz	50.3MHz
0.2μH	159MHz	112MHz	79.6MHz	56.3MHz	35.6MHz
0.4μH	112MHz	79.6MHz	56.2MHz	39.8MHz	22.5MHz
1.0μH	71.2MHz	50.3MHz	35.6MHz	25.2MHz	15.9MHz
2.0μH	50.3MHz	35.6MHz	25.2MHz	17.8MHz	11.3MHz
4.0μH	35.6MHz	25.2MHz	17.8MHz	12.6MHz	7.96MHz
10μH	22.5MHz	15.9MHz	11.2MHz	7.96MHz	5.03MHz
20μH	15.9MHz	11.2MHz	7.96MHz	5.63MHz	3.56MHz
40μH	11.2MHz	7.96MHz	5.62MHz	3.98MHz	2.25MHz
100μH	7.12MHz	5.03MHz	3.56MHz	2.52MHz	1.59MHz
200μH	5.03MHz	3.56MHz	2.52MHz	1.78MHz	1.13MHz
400μH	3.56MHz	2.52MHz	1.78MHz	1.26MHz	796kHz
1mH	2.25MHz	1.59MHz	1.12MHz	796kHz	503kHz

Inductance	50p	100p	200p	400p	1n
1mH	712kHz	503kHz	356kHz	252kHz	159kHz
2mH	503kHz	356kHz	252kHz	178kHz	113kHz
4mH	356kHz	252kHz	178kHz	126kHz	79.6kHz
10mH	225kHz	159kHz	112kHz	79.6kHz	50.3kHz
20mH	159kHz	112kHz	79.6kHz	56.3kHz	35.6kHz
40mH	112kHz	79.6kHz	56.2kHz	39.8kHz	22.5kHz
100mH	71.2kHz	50.3kHz	35.6kHz	25.2kHz	15.9kHz
200mH	50.3kHz	35.6kHz	25.2kHz	17.8kHz	11.3kHz
400mH	35.6kHz	25.2kHz	17.8kHz	12.6kHz	7.96kHz
1H	22.5kHz	15.9kHz	11.2kHz	7.96kHz	5.03kHz

Inductance	500p	1n	2n	4n	10n
10mH	71.2kHz	50.3kHz	35.6kHz	25.2kHz	15.9kHz
20mH	50.3kHz	35.6kHz	25.2kHz	17.8kHz	11.3kHz
40mH	35.6kHz	25.2kHz	17.8kHz	12.6kHz	7.96kHz
100mH	22.5kHz	15.9kHz	11.2kHz	7.96kHz	5.03kHz
200mH	15.9kHz	11.2kHz	7.96kHz	5.63kHz	3.56kHz
400mH	11.2kHz	7.96kHz	5.63kHz	3.98kHz	2.25kHz
1H	7.12kHz	5.03kHz	3.56kHz	2.52kHz	1.59kHz
2H	5.03kHz	3.56kHz	2.52kHz	1.78kHz	1.13kHz
4H	3.56kHz	2.52kHz	1.78kHz	1.26kHz	796Hz
10H	2.25kHz	1.59kHz	1.12kHz	796Hz	503Hz

Inductance	5n	10n	20n	40n	100n
100mH	7.12kHz	5.03kHz	3.56kHz	2.52kHz	1.59kHz
200mH	5.03kHz	3.56kHz	2.52kHz	1.78kHz	1.13kHz
400mH	3.56kHz	2.52kHz	1.78kHz	1.26kHz	796Hz
1H	2.52kHz	1.59kHz	1.12kHz	796Hz	503Hz
2H	1.59kHz	1.12kHz	796Hz	563Hz	356Hz
4H	1.12kHz	796Hz	563Hz	398Hz	225Hz
10H	712Hz	503Hz	356Hz	252Hz	159Hz
20H	503Hz	356Hz	252Hz	178Hz	113Hz
40H	356Hz	252Hz	178Hz	126Hz	79.6Hz
100H	252Hz	159Hz	112Hz	79.6Hz	50.3Hz

Meter Resistors

The sensitivity of a current meter can be reduced if a shunt resistor is used, as in Figure 1.3(a). It can be made to operate as a voltmeter by adding a series resistor, as in Figure 1.3(b). In both cases it is essential to know the resistance of the meter in order to calculate the value of the extra resistor. This formula gives the value for a shunt resistor:

$$R = \frac{\text{Meter R} \times \text{Meter I}}{\text{Required I - Meter I}}$$

For example, if the meter resistance is 100 ohms, its full scale value is 100 milliamps (0.1A), and a full scale value of 1 amp is required, the required shunt resistance is 11.11 ohms ($100 \times 0.1/1 - 0.1 = 11.11$).

The value of a series resistor is calculated by first working out the total resistance through the meter and the series resistor. This is just a matter of applying Ohm's Law, and dividing the required full scale voltage by the meter's full scale current. For instance, suppose that a meter having a full scale value of 1mA (0.001A) must be used as a voltmeter having a full scale value of 100 volts. This gives a total resistance of 100000 ohms ($100V/0.001A = 100000$ ohms), or 100k in other words.

A voltmeter must not draw much current from the main circuit, so it is normally based on a 50µA, 100µA, 500µA, or 1mA meter. The total resistance for meters of these sensitivities is equal to 20k, 10k, 2k, and 1k per full scale volt. Thus our 1mA

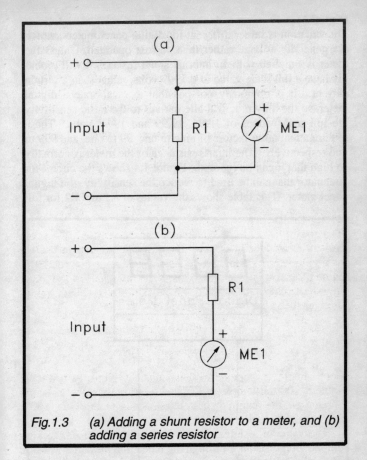

Fig. 1.3   (a) Adding a shunt resistor to a meter, and (b) adding a series resistor

meter requires a total resistance of 100k (100 volts at 1k per volt equals 100k).

Deducting the resistance of the meter gives the value for the series resistor. For instance, if the meter has a resistance of 500 ohms (0.5k), in our example the correct value for the series resistor is 99.5k (100k – 0.5k = 99.5k). With high full scale values the resistance of the meter will be very low in relation to the full resistance of the circuit, and it can then be ignored. In this example the meter's resistance is only 0.5% of the total resistance, which would be insignificant in many applications.

Digital Meters

The situation is rather different for digital panel meters, which are generally voltage rather than current operated. Unless the meter is supplied with an internal shunt resistor, it will probably have a full scale value of 0.1999 volts, rather than a certain current. It is obviously not possible to recalibrate a digital meter, so the only practical alternatives to the basic sensitivity are full scale values of 1.999, 19.99 and 199.9 volts. These require attenuation factors of nine to one, 99 to one, and 999 to one respectively. The input resistance of the meter is normally so high that it can be ignored. Figure 1.4 shows the circuit for attenuator that can be used to reduce the sensitivity of a digital panel meter. This table shows the values of R1 and R2 for full

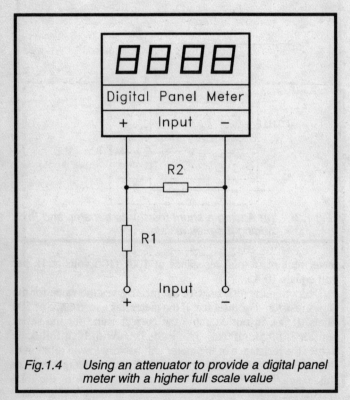

Fig.1.4   *Using an attenuator to provide a digital panel meter with a higher full scale value*

scale values of 1.999, 19.99, and 199.9 volts. In each case the input resistance is over 10M.

Full Scale Voltage	R1	R2
1.999V	10M	1.111M
19.99V	10M	101k
199.9V	10M	10.01k

Obviously the values for R2 are a bit awkward, as none of them are preferred values. The required values must therefore be made up from two or three resistors wired in series. For example, a value of 1.111 megohms can be made by using a 1.1 megohm resistor in series with a 11k component.

Current measurement requires a shunt resistor to be added across the meter, as in Figure 1.5. Again, there are only a limited range of realistic full scale current values since recalibration of a digital meter is not possible. This table shows various full scale values and the shunt resistances required to produce them.

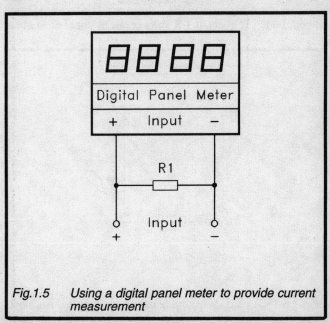

Fig.1.5   *Using a digital panel meter to provide current measurement*

Full Scale Value	Shunt Resistance
19.9µA	100k
199.9µA	10k
1.999mA	1k
19.99mA	100R
199.9mA	10R
1.999A	1R
19.99A	0.1R

L.E.D. Current

Calculating the value of a current limiting resistor for a l.e.d. is very simple, but seems to get many people decidedly vexed. A l.e.d. must normally be fed from the supply, logic output, or whatever, via a series current limiting resistor, as in Figure 1.6. Otherwise the l.e.d. will draw a very high current, possibly damaging both the l.e.d. itself and the driving circuit. The essential point to bear in mind is that the forward voltage across a l.e.d. is much higher than the voltage across a forward biased silicon diode. It is about 1.8 volts or so, as opposed to about

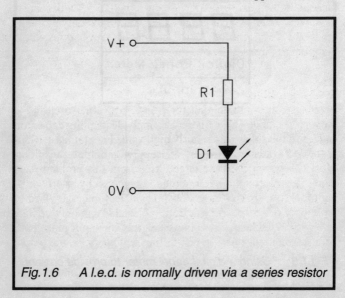

Fig.1.6   A l.e.d. is normally driven via a series resistor

0.6 volts or so for a normal silicon diode. The voltage across the series resistor is therefore about 1.8 volts less than the supply voltage. The first step is to deduct 1.8 volts from the supply voltage to obtain the voltage across the l.e.d. Ohm's Law can then be used to calculate the value of the series resistor, and this is just a matter of dividing the voltage across the resistor by the required l.e.d. current.

Suppose that a l.e.d. must be driven at a current of 10 milliamps (0.01 amps), and that a 9 volt supply is to be used. The voltage across the series resistor will be 7.2 volts (9 – 1.8 volts equals 7.2 volts). Dividing 7.2 volts by 0.01 amps gives a value for the series resistor of 720 ohms. In practice the nearest preferred value above the calculated value often has to be used. In this case a 750 ohm resistor would be used. This gives a typical l.e.d. current of 9.6 milliamps, which should give good results.

Provided the supply voltage is adequate, it is possible to drive two or more l.e.d.s in series, as in Figure 1.7. Remember though, that 1.8 volts per l.e.d. has to be allowed when calculating the voltage across the series resistor. In this example there are three l.e.d.s in series, giving a total of 5.4 volts across the l.e.d.s. With a 9 volt supply this would give only 3.6 volts across the series resistor. A l.e.d. current of 10 milliamps would therefore require a 360 ohm series resistor.

555 Monostable

Figure 1.8 shows the circuit for a basic 555 timer used in the monostable mode. C1 is merely a supply decoupling capacitor, and it is advisable to use a fairly high value here (at least 100µ) as the 555 tends to "crowbar" the supply on output transitions. Most low power 555s are largely free from this problem, and require less decoupling. The circuit is triggered by briefly pulsing pin 2 low. In this case "low" means less than one third of the supply potential. A basic 555 monostable can only operate as a pulse stretcher, so it is important that the input pulse ends before the output pulse in due to finish. Otherwise the output pulse will be elongated.

The output pulse duration is set by R1 and C2, and is equal to 1.1 R1 × C2 seconds. For example, values of 470n and 680k

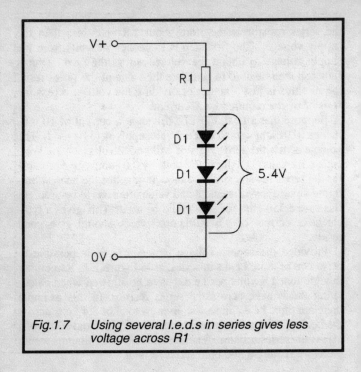

Fig.1.7   Using several l.e.d.s in series gives less voltage across R1

give a pulse duration of 0.35156 seconds (0.47 × 0.68 × 1.1 = 0.35156 seconds). It is generally more convenient to work in megohms and microfarads, rather than ohms and farads, as in this example. A positive output pulse is produced incidentally. R1 should have a value of no more than 20 megohms. The minimum recommended value is 3k, but values down to 1k are generally safe, particularly when low supply voltages are used.

This table shows the output pulse durations for a range of C and R values, and this should aid the selection of suitable values for R1 and C2.

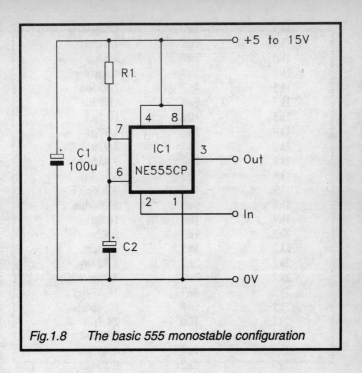

Fig.1.8   The basic 555 monostable configuration

R1	C2	Pulse Duration
1k	1n	1.1µs
1k	1n5	1.65µs
1k	2n2	2.42µs
1k	3n3	3.63µs
1k	4n7	5.17µs
1k	6n8	7.48µs
1k	10n	11µs
1k2	1n	1.32µs
1k2	1n5	1.98µs
1k2	2n2	2.904µs
1k2	3n3	4.356µs
1k2	4n7	6.204µs
1k2	6n8	8.976µs
1k2	10n	13.2µs

11

1k5	1n	1.65μs
1k5	1n5	2.475μs
1k5	2n2	3.63μs
1k5	3n3	4.95μs
1k5	4n7	7.755μs
1k5	6n8	11.22μs
1k5	10n	16.5μs
1k8	1n	1.98μs
1k8	1n5	2.97μs
1k8	2n2	4.356μs
1k8	3n3	6.534μs
1k8	4n7	9.306μs
1k8	6n8	13.464μs
1k8	10n	19.8μs
2k2	1n	2.42μs
2k2	1n5	3.63μs
2k2	2n2	5.324μs
2k2	3n3	7.986μs
2k2	4n7	11.374μs
2k2	6n8	16.456μs
2k2	10n	24.2μs
2k7	1n	2.97μs
2k7	1n5	4.455μs
2k7	2n2	6.534μs
2k7	3n3	9.801μs
2k7	4n7	13.959μs
2k7	6n8	20.196μs
2k7	10n	29.7μs
3k3	1n	3.63μs
3k3	1n5	5.445μs
3k3	2n2	7.986μs
3k3	3n3	11.979μs
3k3	4n7	17.061μs
3k3	6n8	24.684μs
3k3	10n	36.3μs
3k9	1n	4.29μs
3k9	1n5	6.435μs
3k9	2n2	9.438μs
3k9	3n3	14.157μs
3k9	4n7	20.163μs

3k9	6n8	29.172µs
3k9	10n	42.9µs
4k7	1n	5.17µs
4k7	1n5	7.755µs
4k7	2n2	11.374µs
4k7	3n3	17.061µs
4k7	4n7	24.299µs
4k7	6n8	35.156µs
4k7	10n	51.7µs
5k6	1n	6.16µs
5k6	1n5	9.24µs
5k6	2n2	13.552µs
5k6	3n3	21.78µs
5k6	4n7	28.952µs
5k6	6n8	41.888µs
5k6	10n	61.6µs
6k8	1n	7.48µs
6k8	1n5	11.22µs
6k8	2n2	16.456µs
6k8	3n3	24.684µs
6k8	4n7	35.156µs
6k8	6n8	50.864µs
6k8	10n	74.8µs
8k2	1n	9.02µs
8k2	1n5	13.53µs
8k2	2n2	19.844µs
8k2	3n3	29.766µs
8k2	4n7	42.394µs
8k2	6n8	61.336µs
8k2	10n	90.2µs
10k	1n	11µs
10k	1n5	16.5µs
10k	2n2	24.2µs
10k	3n3	36.3µs
10k	4n7	51.7µs
10k	6n8	74.8µs
10k	10n	110µs

Each time the value of R1 or C2 is raised by one decade, the pulse duration is increased by a factor of 10. Thus, a pulse duration of 1.353ms (1353µs) could be obtained using values of 82k and 15n. Values of 820k and 1n5 would provide the same pulse duration, as would values of 8k2 and 150n. Although most low power 555s are accurate at pulse durations down to at 1µs or less, it is advisable to use the standard 555 at pulse durations of no less than 5µs.

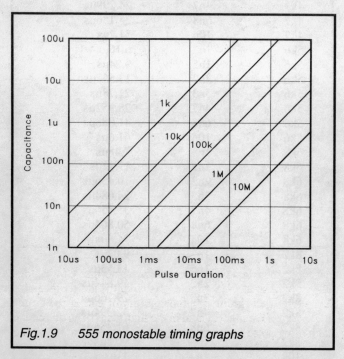

Fig.1.9   555 monostable timing graphs

The graphs of Figure 1.9 also help in the selection of suitable timing values, but these only enable approximate values to be selected. Some calculation or reference to the timing component table will be needed if values are being selected for critical applications.

CMOS Monostables

The circuit diagram for a simple monostable based on two CMOS NOR logic gates is shown in Figure 1.10. This is

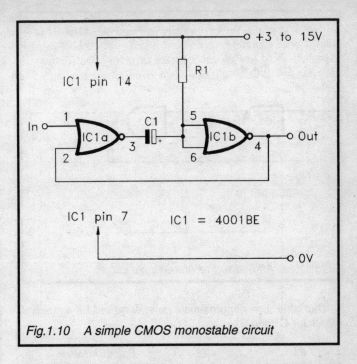

Fig.1.10   A simple CMOS monostable circuit

triggered by a low-to-high transition at normal CMOS logic levels. Unlike the 555 astable, this circuit is not retriggerable. Therefore, each positive output pulse will end at the correct time, even if the input is held in the high state. The duration of the output pulse is not as predictable as that of a 555 monostable. C1 and R1 are the timing components. The pulse duration is approximately 0.65 C1 × R1 seconds. For instance, values of 100k and 10n (0.01μ) would give a pulse time of roughly 0.65ms (0.1M × 0.01μ × 0.65 = 0.00065 seconds, or 0.65ms).

Figure 1.11 shows the circuit diagram for an alternative form of CMOS monostable. This is based on two CMOS NAND gates. It is triggered on a high-to-low transition, and the output pulses low when the circuit is triggered. As before, the duration of the output pulse is approximately 0.65 C1 × R1 seconds. R1 can have any value from about 4k7 upwards.

15

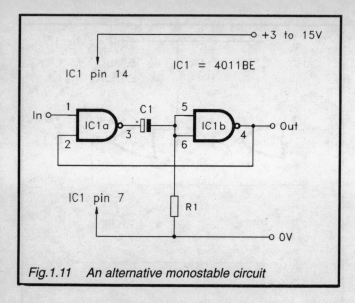

Fig.1.11   An alternative monostable circuit

This table shows approximate pulse durations for a range of values for C1 and R1.

R1	C1	Pulse Duration
10k	1n	0.65μs
10k	1n5	0.975μs
10k	2n2	1.43μs
10k	3n3	2.145μs
10k	4n7	3.005μs
10k	6n8	4.42μs
10k	10n	6.5μs
12k	1n	0.78μs
12k	1n5	1.17μs
12k	2n2	1.716μs
12k	3n3	2.574μs
12k	4n7	4.507μs
12k	6n8	5.304μs
12k	10n	7.8μs
15k	1n	0.975μs
15k	1n5	1.462μs

15k	2n2	2.145µs
15k	3n3	3.217µs
15k	4n7	4.582µs
15k	6n8	6.63µs
15k	10n	9.75µs
18k	1n	1.17µs
18k	1n5	1.755µs
18k	2n2	2.574µs
18k	3n3	3.861µs
18k	4n7	5.499µs
18k	6n8	7.956µs
18k	10n	11.7µs
22k	1n	1.43µs
22k	1n5	2.145µs
22k	2n2	3.146µs
22k	3n3	4.719µs
22k	4n7	6.721µs
22k	6n8	9.724µs
22k	10n	14.3µs
27k	1n	1.755µs
27k	1n5	2.632µs
27k	2n2	3.861µs
27k	3n3	5.791µs
27k	4n7	8.248µs
27k	6n8	11.934µs
27k	10n	17.55µs
33k	1n	2.145µs
33k	1n5	3.217µs
33k	2n2	4.719µs
33k	3n3	7.078µs
33k	4n7	10.081µs
33k	6n8	14.586µs
33k	10n	21.45µs
39k	1n	2.535µs
39k	1n5	3.802µs
39k	2n2	5.577µs
39k	3n3	8.365µs
39k	4n7	11.914µs
39k	6n8	17.238µs
39k	10n	25.35µs

47k	1n	3.055µs
47k	1n5	4.582µs
47k	2n2	6.721µs
47k	3n3	10.081µs
47k	4n7	14.358µs
47k	6n8	20.774µs
47k	10n	30.55µs
56k	1n	3.64µs
56k	1n5	5.46µs
56k	2n2	8.008µs
56k	3n3	12.012µs
56k	4n7	17.108µs
56k	6n8	24.752µs
56k	10n	36.4µs
68k	1n	4.42µs
68k	1n5	6.63µs
68k	2n2	9.724µs
68k	3n3	14.586µs
68k	4n7	20.774µs
68k	6n8	30.056µs
68k	10n	44.2µs
82k	1n	5.33µs
82k	1n5	7.995µs
82k	2n2	11.726µs
82k	3n3	17.589µs
82k	4n7	25.051µs
82k	6n8	43.706µs
82k	10n	53.3µs
100k	1n	6.5µs
100k	1n5	9.75µs
100k	2n2	14.3µs
100k	3n3	21.45µs
100k	4n7	30.05s
100k	6n8	44.2µs
100k	10n	65µs

The timing graphs of Figure 1.12 are useful when selecting timing component values for the two CMOS monostables, but they only enable approximate values to be determined.

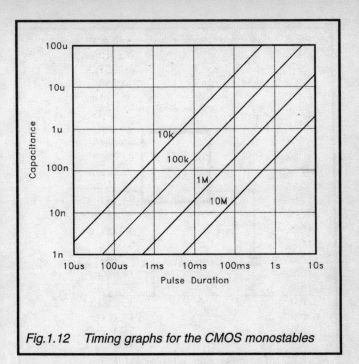

Fig.1.12   Timing graphs for the CMOS monostables

555 Astable

The circuit diagram for a basic 555 astable (oscillator) appears in Figure 1.13. Like the 555 monostable, it is advisable to use a large decoupling capacitor if a standard 555 is used. In theory it is necessary to include C3 to filter out stray pick-up at the modulation input of the 555. In practice this capacitor is normally omitted, with no signs of any ill effects.

The output waveform at pin 3 of IC1 is a pulse signal, but for a normal 555 astable it is never a squarewave. This is due to the way in which the timing circuit functions. The timing components are R1, R2, and C2. C2 charges to two thirds of the supply voltage via R1 and R2, and then discharges to one third of the supply potential by way of R2 and an internal transistor of the 555. The circuit oscillates indefinitely in this fashion, with the charge on C2 going to and fro between one-third and two-thirds of the supply voltage. The output at pin 3

19

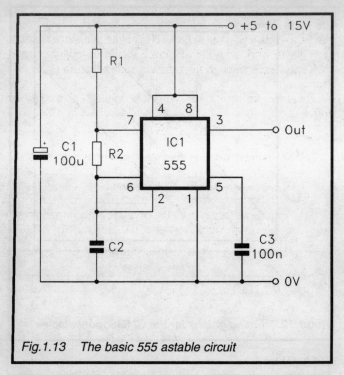

Fig.1.13   The basic 555 astable circuit

is high while C2 is charging, and low when it is discharging. The output of the standard circuit can not be a squarewave because C2 charges through R1 and R2, but only discharges through R2. This results in a charge time which is longer than the discharge time, although making the value of R1 low in comparison to that of R2 minimises the disparity. The operating frequency is equal to:

$$f = 1.44/\{(R1 + 2R2)\ C2\}$$

As a simple example, suppose that C2 has a value of 10n, and that R1 and R2 are respectively 10k and 100k components. First the total effective timing resistance must be calculated. This is equal to twice 100k plus 10k, which is clearly 210k (0.21M). This is multiplied by the value of C2, which is 0.01µ, giving an answer of 0.0021. Finally, dividing 1.44 by this figure gives the operating frequency in hertz. According to my calculator this works out at 685.71Hz. Note that, once again, it is easier to work with the resistance values in megohms, and the capacitance value in microfarads, rather than in ohms and farads.

The time for which the output is high is given by the formula:

$$t = 0.693 \ (R1 + R2) \ C2 \ \text{seconds}$$

The low output period is given by the formula:

$$t = 0.693 \ R2 \times C2 \ \text{seconds}$$

Applying these formulas to the example values used previously, the high output time works out at $0.11M \times 0.01\mu \times 0.693$,

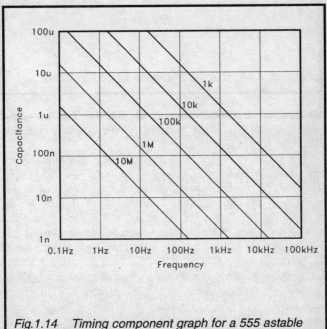

Fig.1.14 *Timing component graph for a 555 astable*

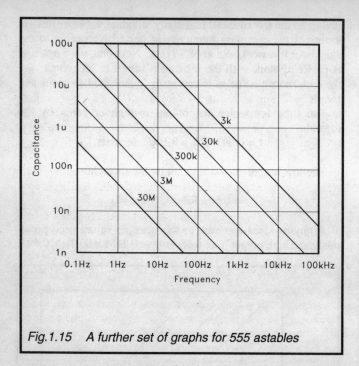

Fig.1.15   A further set of graphs for 555 astables

which equals 0.0007623 seconds, or 762.3μs. The low output period is equal to 0.1M × 0.01μ × 0.693, which comes to 0.000693 seconds, or 693μs.

The graphs of Figures 1.14 and 1.15 are useful when selecting suitable values for the timing components in a 555 astable. These show the frequencies produced by a range of timing resistances and capacitances. Note that the resistances are the total timing resistances (i.e R1 plus 2 × R2). For example, a timing resistance of about 100k would be produced using 33k resistors for R1 and R2, and a 30k total timing resistance would be produced using a value of 10k for both R1 and R2. When using these graphs it is essential to bear in mind that both the capacitance and frequency axes are logarithmic. The graphs will only give a rough indication of the timing values needed for a given output frequency, and where necessary some calculations will be needed in order to "fine tune" the values to ones that will give the required frequency with a suitable degree of accuracy.

Wien Oscillator

Figure 1.16 shows the basic circuit for Wien oscillator, or Wien bridge oscillator as it is also known. IC1 is an operational amplifier that is used in the non-inverting mode. R3, R5, C3 and C4 form a phase shift network which provides frequency selective feedback over the amplifier. At a certain frequency there is zero phase shift through this Wien network, and positive feedback is applied over the amplifier. Provided the gain of the amplifier is greater than the losses through the Wien network at this frequency, the circuit will oscillate.

A closed loop voltage gain of only about three times is needed in order to produce oscillation. The output waveform is a high quality sinewave, but only if the gain of the amplifier is maintained at a level which is just about adequate to sustain oscillation. Slightly lower gain causes oscillation to subside and then cease altogether. A slight excess of gain results in a severely clipped output signal that is more like a low grade squarewave than a sinewave signal. In this circuit the value of VR1 is carefully adjusted to a setting that gives a good quality output signal. Better results are obtained using an RA53 thermistor to provide gain stabilisation. The RA53 is connected in place of VR1 and R6, and the value of R4 must be reduced to about 680R. The modified circuit is shown in Figure 1.17. The output level is about one volt r.m.s. (2.8 volts peak-to-peak).

The operating frequency of the circuit is controlled by R3, R5, C3, and C4. In a practical circuit the value of R3 is normally equal to that of R5, and the two capacitors also have the same value. The operating frequency is then given by the formula:

$$f = 1/6.283 \, C \, R \text{ hertz}$$

The graphs of Figure 1.18 are a useful to finding suitable C – R values, but this will only provide a rough guide to component selection. This table shows a range of approximate C – R values for various output frequencies, and should also prove helpful.

23

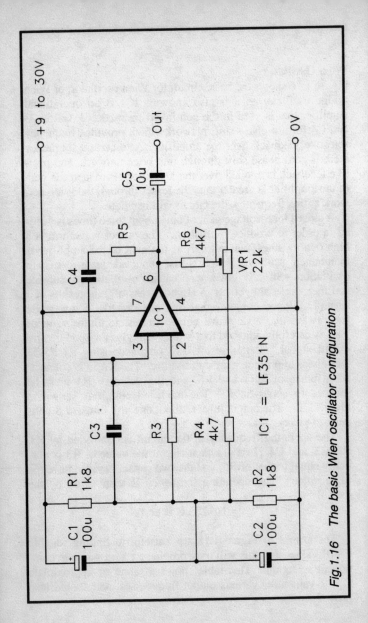

Fig.1.16 The basic Wien oscillator configuration

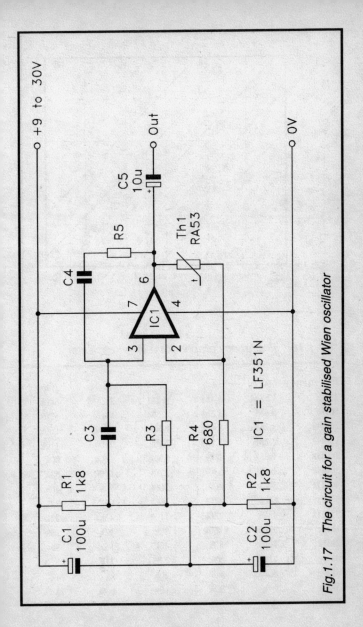

Fig.1.17 The circuit for a gain stabilised Wien oscillator

25

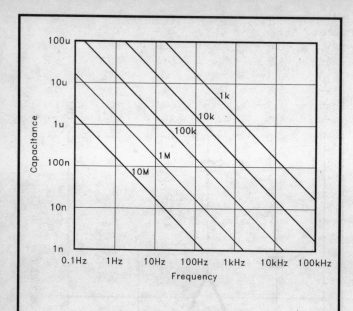

Fig.1.18   Frequency graphs for a Wien oscillator

Frequency	500p	1n	2n	5n	10n
25Hz	12.8M	6.4M	3.2M	1.28M	640k
50Hz	6.4M	3.2M	1.6M	640k	320k
100Hz	3.2M	1.6M	800k	320k	160k
150Hz	2.2M	1.1M	530k	220k	110k
200Hz	1.6M	800k	400k	160k	80k
300Hz	1.1M	530k	270k	110k	53k
400Hz	800k	400k	200k	80k	40k
500Hz	640k	320k	160k	64k	32k
750Hz	430k	220k	110k	43k	22k
1kHz	320k	160k	80k	32k	16k
2kHz	160k	80k	40k	16k	8k
3kHz	110k	53k	27k	11k	5.3k
4kHz	80k	40k	20k	8k	4k
5kHz	64k	32k	16k	6.4k	3.2k
7.5kHz	43k	22k	11k	4.3k	2.2k

10kHz	32k	16k	8k	3.2k	1.6k
20kHz	16k	8k	4k	1.6k	800R
50kHz	6.4k	3.2k	1.6k	640R	320R
100kHz	3.2k	1.6k	800R	320R	160R

Frequency	*20n*	*50n*	*100n*	*200n*	*500n*
25Hz	320k	160k	64k	32k	12.8k
50Hz	160k	64k	32k	16k	6.4k
100Hz	80k	32k	16k	8k	3.2k
150Hz	53k	22k	11k	5.3k	2.2k
200Hz	40k	16k	8k	4k	1.6k
300Hz	27k	11k	5.3k	2.7k	1.1k
400Hz	20k	8k	4k	2k	800R
500Hz	16k	6.4k	3.2k	1.6k	640R
750Hz	11k	4.3k	2.2k	1.1k	430R
1kHz	8k	3.2k	1.6k	800R	320R
2kHz	4k	1.6k	800R	400R	160R
3kHz	2.7k	1.1k	530R	270R	110R
4kHz	2k	800R	400R	200R	80R
5kHz	1.6k	640R	320R	160R	64R
7.5kHz	1.1k	430R	220R	110R	43R
10kHz	800R	320R	160R	80R	32R
20kHz	400R	160R	80R	40R	16R
50kHz	160R	64R	32R	16R	6.4R
100kHz	80R	32R	16R	8R	3.2R

Basic C – R Filters

The circuits of Figure 1.19 are for basic lowpass (a) and high-pass (b) filters having an ultimate attenuation rate of 6dB per octave. In other words, for the lowpass filter a doubling of frequency produces a doubling of the circuit's losses. In the case of the highpass filter, a halving of the input frequency produces a doubling of the circuit's losses. The introduction of the attenuation is relatively gradual with these simple passive filters. The cutoff frequency of a highpass or lowpass filter is the frequency where the response reaches the –3dB point. For both types of filter the cutoff frequency is given by the formula:

$$f = 1/2\pi \, R \times C$$

27

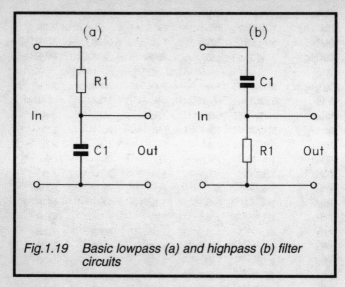

*Fig.1.19   Basic lowpass (a) and highpass (b) filter
circuits*

This can be simplified to:-

$$f = 1.59/R \times C$$

Thus values of 10k and 10n would give a cutoff frequency at 1.59kHz ($0.01M \times 0.01\mu = 0.001$, 1.59 divided by 0.001 equals 1590Hz, or 1.59kHz).   As usual, it is easier to work in megohms and microfarads, rather than ohms and farads. The required resistance for a given capacitance value and cutoff frequency can be obtained using this formula:

$$R = 0.159/f \times C$$

For instance, suppose that a cutoff frequency of 3kHz is required, and a capacitance value of 10n has been selected as a starting point. Multiplying the frequency by the capacitance value gives an answer of 30 ($3000Hz \times 0.01\mu = 30$). Dividing 0.159 by 30 gives the required resistance value of 0.0053 megohms, or 5.3k in other words. The nearest preferred value of 5.1k would therefore be used.

This table gives approximate cutoff frequencies for a range of values for R1 and C1.

Capacitance	1k	2k	5k	10k	20k
10p	16MHz	8MHz	3.2MHz	1.6MHz	800kHz
20p	8MHz	4MHz	1.6MHz	800kHz	400kHz
50p	3.2MHz	1.6MHz	640kHz	320kHz	160kHz
100p	1.6MHz	800kHz	320kHz	160kHz	80kHz
200p	800kHz	400kHz	160kHz	80kHz	40kHz
500p	320kHz	160kHz	64kHz	32kHz	16kHz
1n	160kHz	80kHz	32kHz	16kHz	8kHz
2n	80kHz	40kHz	16kHz	8kHz	4kHz
5n	32kHz	16kHz	6.4kHz	3.2kHz	1.6kHz
10n	16kHz	8kHz	3.2kHz	1.6kHz	800Hz
20n	8kHz	4kHz	1.6kHz	800Hz	400Hz
50n	3.2kHz	1.6kHz	640Hz	320Hz	160Hz
100n	1.6kHz	800Hz	320Hz	160Hz	80Hz
200n	800Hz	400Hz	160Hz	80Hz	40Hz
500n	320Hz	160Hz	64Hz	32Hz	16Hz
1µ	160Hz	80Hz	32Hz	16Hz	8Hz
2µ	80Hz	40Hz	16Hz	8Hz	4Hz
5µ	32Hz	16Hz	6.4Hz	3.2Hz	1.6Hz
10µ	16Hz	8Hz	3.2Hz	1.6Hz	0.8Hz
20µ	8Hz	4Hz	1.6Hz	0.8Hz	0.4Hz
50µ	3.2Hz	1.6Hz	0.64Hz	0.32Hz	0.16Hz
10µ	1.6Hz	0.8Hz	0.32Hz	0.16Hz	0.08Hz

Capacitance	50k	100k	200k	500k	1M
10p	320kHz	160kHz	80kHz	32kHz	16kHz
20p	160kHz	80kHz	40kHz	16kHz	8kHz
50p	64kHz	32kHz	16kHz	6.4kHz	3.2kHz
100p	32kHz	16kHz	8kHz	3.2kHz	1.6kHz
200p	16kHz	8kHz	4kHz	1.6kHz	800Hz
500p	6.4kHz	3.2kHz	1.6kHz	640Hz	320Hz
1n	3.2kHz	1.6kHz	800Hz	320Hz	160Hz
2n	1.6kHz	800Hz	400Hz	160Hz	80H
5n	640Hz	320Hz	160Hz	64Hz	32Hz
10n	320Hz	160Hz	80Hz	32Hz	16Hz
20n	160Hz	80Hz	40Hz	16Hz	8Hz
50n	64Hz	32Hz	16Hz	6.4Hz	3.2Hz
100n	32Hz	16Hz	8Hz	3.2Hz	1.6Hz
200n	16Hz	8Hz	4Hz	1.6Hz	0.8Hz
500n	6.4Hz	3.2Hz	1.6Hz	0.64Hz	0.32Hz

1μ	3.2Hz	1.6Hz	0.8Hz	0.32Hz	0.16Hz
2μ	1.6Hz	0.8Hz	0.4Hz	0.16Hz	0.08Hz
5μ	0.64Hz	0.32Hz	0.16Hz	0.064Hz	0.032Hz
10μ	0.32Hz	0.16Hz	0.08Hz	0.032Hz	0.016Hz

The graphs of Figures 1.20 to 1.22 are helpful when determining approximate values for basic highpass and lowpass filters. Bear in mind that the frequency axis and the capacitance axis both have logarithmic scaling.

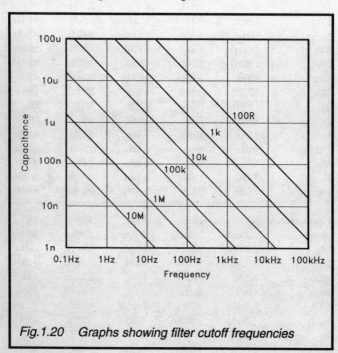

Fig.1.20   Graphs showing filter cutoff frequencies

Twin T Filter

The circuit of Figure 1.23 is for a twin T filter. The reason for its name should be readily apparent when looking at the circuit. This is a passive filter which provides a deep notch of attenuation. In practice it is normally necessary to use a buffer amplifier at the output, so that the filter "looks" into a suitably high

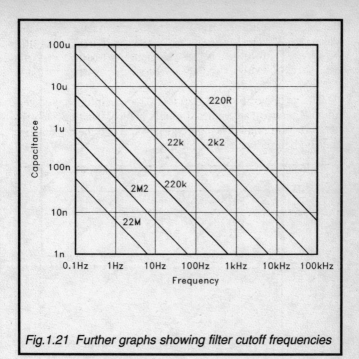

Fig.1.21 Further graphs showing filter cutoff frequencies

load impedance. In this case IC1 acts as the output buffer stage, and biasing is provided by R1 and R2 via the resistors in the filter circuit. R3 and R5 must be equal in value, and have twice the resistance of R4. C2 and C4 should be equal in value, and have half the value of C3. This can be difficult using preferred values.

The usual solution is to make up R4 from two resistors wired in parallel, with each resistor having the same value as R3/5. Similarly, C3 can be made up from two capacitors in parallel which each have the same value as C2/C4. Figure 1.24 shows an example circuit of this type. In some applications it is necessary to use a preset resistor for R4, so that it can be adjusted for optimum attenuation at the notch frequency. The notch frequency is given by the formula:

$$f = 1.59/R3 \times C2$$

31

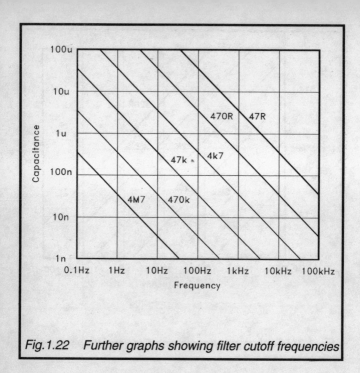

Fig.1.22   Further graphs showing filter cutoff frequencies

For instance, suppose that this set of values is used in a twin T filter:

R3/5	160k
R4	80k
C2/4	10n
C3	20n

Multiplying the value of R3 by that of C2 gives a figure of 0.0016 (0.16M × 0.01μ equals 0.0016). Dividing 0.159 by this figure gives an answer of 99.375 hertz. The filter would therefore produce a notch of deep attenuation at a frequency of about 100Hz.

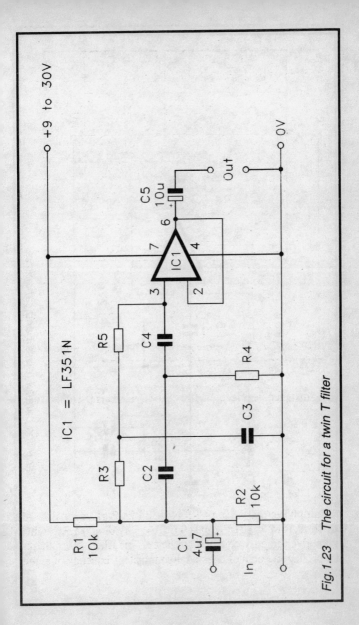

Fig. 1.23   The circuit for a twin T filter

33

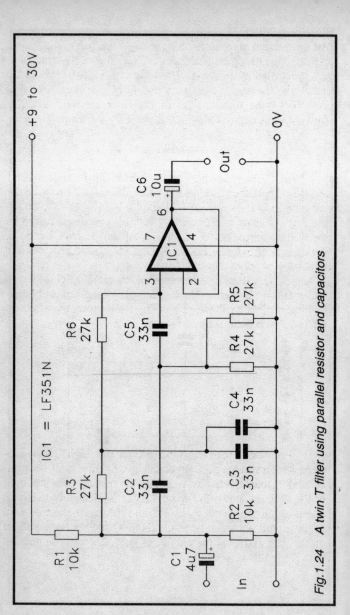

Fig. 1.24 A twin T filter using parallel resistor and capacitors

Bandpass Filter

An operational amplifier can be used as the basis of a simple but effective bandpass filter. Figure 1.25 shows the configuration for a filter of this type. The values of R1, R4, C1, and C2 determine the centre frequency and Q of the filter. For a Q value of 1 the mathematics of the filter are very straightforward. The centre frequency is given by the formula:

$$f = 1.59/R \times C$$

C1 and C2 have a value equal to "C" in this formula, but R1 should be half the value of "R", and R4 should be twice the value of "R". If the value of R1 and R4 is equal to "R", the filter has a Q value of 0.5, and its voltage gain drops from two times to 0.5 times. As an example, a value of 1n for C1 and C2, plus values of 5k6 and 22k for R1 and R4, would give a centre frequency of approximately 1kHz.

Higher Q values can be obtained by making R1 lower in value, and R4 higher in value. Higher Q gives reduced bandwidth and higher voltage gain. This table shows the effect of R1 and R4 on both of these factors.

R1	R4	Q	V. GAIN
1×	1×	0.5	0.5
0.5×	2×	1	2
0.25×	4×	2	8
0.125×	8×	4	32
0.0625×	16×	8	128

It is inevitable with this type of filter that high Q also produces a high voltage gain. In practice this gain is often unwanted, and is counteracted by an additional resistor near the input of the filter, as shown in Figure 1.26. R5 effectively forms an attenuator in conjunction with R1, and reduces the overall gain of the circuit accordingly. Note though, that R5 has an effect on the gain and Q of the circuit, as it is effectively in parallel with R1 in this respect.

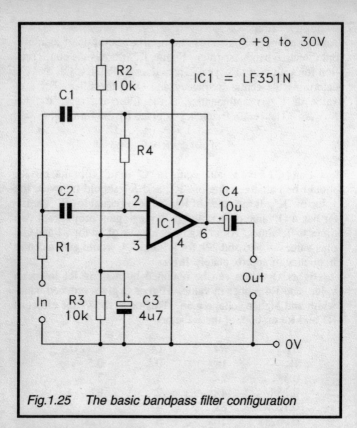

Fig.1.25   The basic bandpass filter configuration

State-Variable Filter

Figure 1.27 shows the circuit diagram for a state-variable filter. This provides bandpass, notch, highpass, and lowpass responses, with a separate output for each one. The highpass and lowpass responses provide second order (12dB per octave) responses. The operating frequency is set by C3, C4, R7, and R10. The centre frequency is given by the "standard" formula:

$$f = 0.159/R \times C$$

The tables, etc., provided earlier pertaining to basic lowpass and highpass filters can also be used to aid the selection of

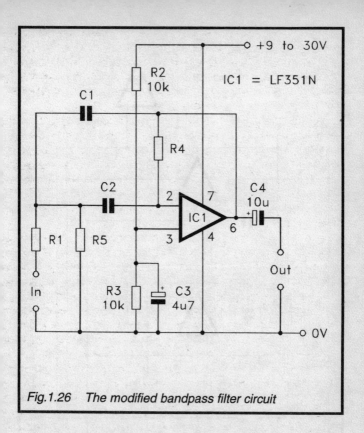

Fig.1.26   The modified bandpass filter circuit

suitable values for this state-variable filter. The value of R8 controls the Q of the circuit, and the value for R8 is obtained by multiplying the required Q value by 10k (e.g. a value of 51k for a Q of approximately five). R6 should be replaced with a 22k trimpot if a very high degree of attenuation is required at the notch output. The trimpot is adjusted for optimum balance of the two input signals to IC2b, and well over 80dB of attenuation should be possible.

Power Supplies
Modern electronics tends to be extremely complex, but many circuits can still be battery powered due to the low current

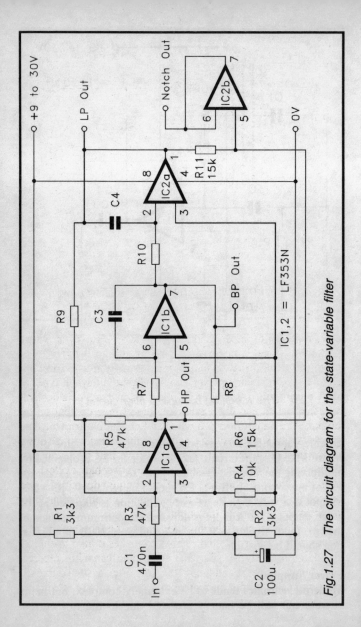

Fig.1.27   The circuit diagram for the state-variable filter

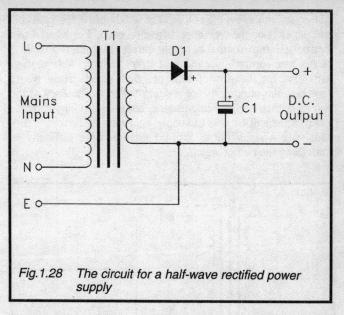

consumptions of most integrated circuits. However, where
portability is not a major consideration it is still likely to be
more economic to use a mains power supply unit. The most
simple type of mains power supply is the half-wave type, as
shown in Figure 1.28. This is little used in practice since it is
very inefficient and has a relatively high ripple content on the
output. The transformer provides safety isolation from the dan-
gerous mains supply voltage, and steps the mains voltage down
to the required level. D1 enables positive half cycles to pass
through to the output, but it blocks negative half cycles. As
with any of the standard rectifier circuits described here,
reversing the polarity of the diode(s) and smoothing capacitor
reverses the polarity of the output supply.

The inefficiency of the circuit is due to the fact that the negative half cycles are wasted. This also makes it hard to smooth
the d.c. output signal, since the smoothing capacitor receives
only 50 pulses per second, not 100. It is often assumed that the
maximum d.c. output current from a power supply is equal to
the secondary current rating of the mains transformer, but

matters are not as simple as this. The maximum d.c. output current depends on the type of rectification used. For a half-wave rectifier the maximum d.c. output current is equal to just 28% of the transformer's secondary current rating. This renders half-wave rectification of little practical value except where very low output currents are required. The inefficiency of the circuit is then of little importance, since even a small mains transformer will be able to supply an excess of current. Also, with only a small output current there is little difficulty in smoothing the output signal.

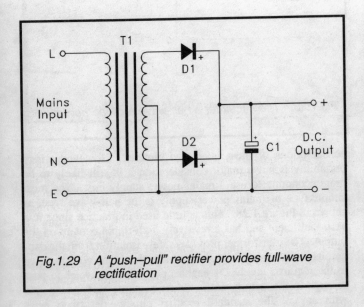

Fig.1.29   A "push–pull" rectifier provides full-wave rectification

Figure 1.29 shows the circuit for a basic full-wave power supply which uses two rectifiers in what is sometimes called a "push-pull" rectifier. The mains transformer must be a centre-tapped type, or have twin secondaries connected in series to give what is effectively a centre-tapped secondary. The circuit is basically just two half-wave circuits operating in anti-phase. D1 and D2 therefore supply pulses to smoothing capacitor C1 on alternate half cycles, giving full-wave rectification.

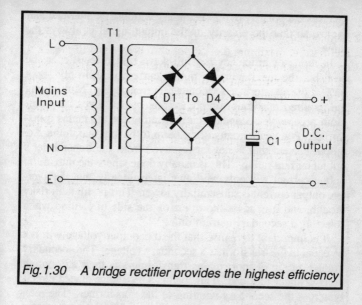

Fig.1.30   A bridge rectifier provides the highest efficiency

This might not seem to be much better than half-wave rectification, but the fact that it provides full-wave rectification makes it easier to smooth the d.c. output signal. Also, each half-wave section of the circuit greatly reduces the burden on the other section, giving increased efficiency. The maximum d.c. output current is equal to the secondary current rating of the transformer. This is not to say that the circuit is 100% efficient. The output voltage is only half that which would be obtained if the full secondary winding was used to drive a half-wave or bridge rectifier. The circuit is therefore about 50% efficient, which is still a great improvement over a half-wave circuit.

The circuit for a full-wave power supply using bridge rectification is shown in Figure 1.30. The four rectifiers steer the output of the transformer through to the output with the correct polarity, regardless of the polarity of the output signal from the transformer. The top right and bottom left rectifiers conduct when the top end of the winding is positive going, while the other two rectifiers conduct when the top end of the secondary winding is negative going. It is rather like having a switch that

41

reverses the polarity of the secondary winding on alternate half cycles, so that the polarity of the output signal is always the same.

In terms of efficiency the full-wave bridge rectifier is the best, but the maximum d.c. output current is still only about 62% of the transformer's secondary current rating. Multiplying the required maximum output current by 1.6 gives the minimum acceptable secondary current rating for the mains transformer. Practical circuits often seem to have a maximum d.c. output current that is not far removed from the transformer's output current rating. This is usually done where the maximum output current will only be drawn intermittently, and the average output current is substantially lower. This is still a bit risky though, and it is advisable to err on the side of caution when selecting a secondary current rating.

It is important to realise that the d.c. output voltage will not be equal to the transformer's secondary voltage. The secondary voltage rating of most mains transformers is their a.c. output voltage under full load. This load is a resistance placed directly across the secondary winding of the transformer. The rectified and smoothed output voltage is equal to the peak output voltage from the transformer, minus the voltage drop through the rectifier circuit. The peak output voltage from the transformer is 1.41 times the r.m.s. value. The voltage drop through the rectifier circuit is about 0.7 volts for half-wave and push-pull circuits, and about 1.4 volts for bridge rectifiers. The voltage drops tend to be somewhat higher for high current supplies. Typical voltages drops are 1.1 and 2.2 volts respectively at currents of about one to two amps.

The loaded output voltage from a 12 volt transformer using bridge rectification would therefore be about 15.52 volts (12 volts × 1.41 equals 16.92, 16.92 − 1.4 equals 15.52 volts). For a high current supply the output voltage would be a little lower, at just under 15 volts. The mains transformer only supplies current on the peaks of half cycles where the output voltage of the rectifier exceeds the voltage across the smoothing capacitor. The mains transformer is therefore providing short bursts of high current, and it is heavily loaded during these current pulses. This tends to reduce the d.c. output voltage from the circuit. Practical tests on a few mains transformers suggest that this gives a reduction in the loaded output voltage of about 10% or so. Thus the actual output voltage from our example power supply would be about 14 volts.

The unloaded supply potential is much higher than the loaded output voltage, and is typically about 30% to 35% higher. In this example the unloaded output voltage would therefore be about 18 volts or so. The exact figure depends on the precise characteristics of the mains transformer used.

Rectifiers

The half-wave and push-pull circuits require rectifiers that have a peak inverse voltage (p.i.v.) rating of at least double the unloaded d.c. output voltage. It is a common mistake to assume that the rectifiers only need a voltage rating equal to or greater than the normal d.c. output voltage of the circuit. However, the rectifiers must be able to handle the unloaded output voltage, which will be substantially higher than the loaded figure. Of greater significance, on negative half cycles the anode (−) terminal of each rectifier is taken to a negative potential roughly equal to the positive potential on the cathode. These two potentials add together, giving a peak voltage across each rectifier that is roughly double the d.c. output voltage. It is advisable to choose a rectifier that has a p.i.v. rating of at least four times the secondary voltage rating of the mains transformer. 100 volt rectifiers would therefore be satisfactory when using a 24 volt transformer.

A bridge rectifier can be made up from four separate rectifiers, or a bridge rectifier module can be used. If separate rectifiers are utilized, they should have a p.i.v. rating equal to at least four times the mains transformer's secondary voltage. The voltage ratings quoted for bridge rectifiers are normally the p.i.v. ratings of the rectifiers within the bridge, and not the maximum a.c. input potential or d.c. output voltage. Once again, the rectifier must have a voltage rating equal to at least four times the secondary voltage rating of the mains transformer.

The maximum current rating for a rectifier, whether a bridge type or a single rectifier, is the maximum permissible average current flow. Simply choose a rectifier that has a current rating that is at least equal to the maximum d.c. output current that will be drawn from the supply.

43

This table provides some basic data for a number of common rectifiers.

Type	PIV	Current	Max V. Drop
1N4001	50V	1A	1.1V
1N4002	100V	1A	1.1V
1N4003	200V	1A	1.1V
1N4004	400V	1A	1.1V
1N4005	600V	1A	1.1V
1N4006	800V	1A	1.1V
1N4007	1000V	1A	1.1V
1N5400	50V	3A	1.1V
1N5401	100V	3A	1.1V
1N5402	200V	3A	1.1V
1N5404	400V	3A	1.1V
1N5406	600V	3A	1.1V
1N5407	800V	3A	1.1V
1N5408	1000V	3A	1.1V
MR751	100V	6A	1.1V
MR752	200V	6A	1.1V
MR754	400V	6A	1.1V
MR756	600V	6A	1.1V
MR78	800V	6A	1.1V
P600A	50V	6A	0.9V
P600D	200V	6A	0.9V
P600J	600V	6A	0.9V
R250S	800V	6A	1.1V
1N5820	20V	3A	0.525V
1N5822	40V	3A	0.525V
MBR1090	90V	10A	0.57V

The voltage drop is at the maximum rated current of the device, and is a worse case figure not a typical one. The 1N5820, 1N5822, and MBR1090 are Schottky rectifiers. In addition to their low voltage drops they also have fast switching times, making them well suited to operation in switch mode power supplies. Figure 1.31 provides leadout details for a range of rectifiers, including some obsolete types which might be encountered when servicing older equipment.

44

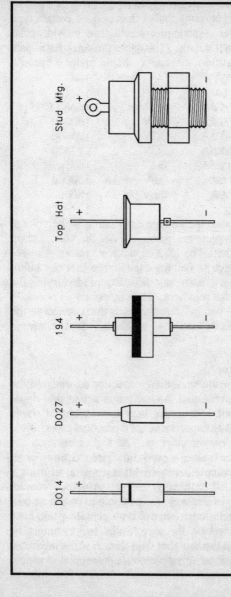

Fig. 1.31   Leadout details for most rectifiers, old and new

Bridge rectifiers are sometimes sold on the basis of a particular voltage and current rating, rather than under a certain type number. The retailer's catalogue should then provide brief data, including leadout details. This table provides basic data for a few bridge rectifiers that are available under a specific type number.

Type	PIV	Current	V. Drop	Load C Max
W005	50V	1.5A	2.2V	5000μ
W01	100V	1.5A	2.2V	2500μ
W02	200V	1.5A	2.2V	1250μ
W04	400V	1.5A	2.2V	625μ
PW01	100V	6A	2.6V (@ 3A)	5000μ
PW04	400V	6A	2.6V (@ 3A)	800μ

Note that in this case the voltage drop rating is the voltage drop through the complete bridge circuit, not the voltage drop per individual rectifier. The load capacitance rating is effectively the highest value smoothing capacitance that can safely be used. There is not usually any difficulty in identifying the leadout wires of bridge rectifiers. The component is normally marked "AC" or " ~ " to indicate the leads that connect to the a.c. input signal, and "+" and "−" to identify the d.c. output terminals.

Smoothing Capacitor
The correct value for the smoothing capacitor depends on the maximum output current, and the maximum acceptable ripple voltage on the output. Obtaining very low values of ripple using a large smoothing capacitor is not a practical proposition, except at very low output currents. At higher currents the required capacitance value would be impractically large. Where a low ripple supply is required it is a matter of using a voltage regulator to electronically smooth the output from an unregulated supply. In this way it is possible to obtain an output noise level of well under one millivolt peak-to-peak, even though the ripple level on the unregulated supply might be more than a thousand times higher than this. It is not advisable to have a very high level of ripple on the unregulated supply even if a regulator circuit will be used. With a few volts of

ripple it would be almost certain that the input voltage to the regulator would drop below the minimum acceptable level, the drop-out voltage, on negative ripple peaks.

The voltage rating of the smoothing capacitor must be at least equal to the unloaded d.c. output voltage of the supply. It is advisable to be generous with the voltage rating of the smoothing capacitor, since a breakdown in this component could result in it drawing a very high current. This could in turn result in it literally exploding! I would recommend using a component that has a voltage rating at least double the loaded output voltage of the supply. For a loaded output of about 12 volts a 25 volt capacitor would therefore be used.

The ripple current rating of capacitors is a factor that tends to be overlooked. There is a limit to the maximum current that a capacitor can have flowing in and out as it smooths the supply. As one would expect, this ripple current rating tends to be low for small capacitors, and high for high value types. Although a large amount of ripple on the supply's output might be perfectly acceptable, the capacitor selected might not have a high enough ripple current rating. A low voltage 470µ component, for example, typically has a ripple current rating of under 500 milliamps. Although a value of 470µ might give perfectly adequate smoothing, it might be necessary to settle for a much higher value in order to achieve a high enough ripple current rating. For an output current of 1 amp a value of at least 1000µ would be required, and a value of 2200µ would be a safer option.

As a general "rule of thumb", it is necessary to have a smoothing capacitance of at least 1µ per milliamp of output current, and preferably 2.2µ per milliamp of output current. It would often be advantageous to have a very high value smoothing capacitor. However, values of more than about 10000µ are difficult to obtain, even in low voltage types. Capacitors having voltage ratings of about 40 volts or more are difficult to obtain in values of more than about 4700µ. The very high value capacitors that can be obtained tend to be both bulky and expensive. This often forces a compromise, with reduced smoothing being used, together with a higher loaded input voltage to the regulator.

Practical experience suggests that good results will be

obtained if the smoothing capacitor has a value equal to at least 2µ per milliamp of output current, and the loaded voltage across the smoothing capacitor is at least 25% higher than the drop-out voltage of the of the regulator.

Voltage Regulators

For most purposes ordinary three terminal monolithic voltage regulators are the most convenient type. They are available in a range of popular output voltages, in both positive and negative versions. They are used in the simple circuit configuration of Figure 1.32. There is little that is problematic when using these regulators, as they are very stable and reliable. However, to guarantee stability the two decoupling capacitors (C1 and C2) must be positioned close to the regulator chip. C1 and C2 should be ceramic capacitors, or another type that works well at high frequencies. The circuit diagram of Figure 1.32 is for positive regulator, but for a negative supply it is merely necessary to use a 79** series regulator instead of a 78** type. Figure 1.33 shows the circuit diagram for a negative voltage regulator.

Performance figures vary somewhat from one device in the series to another, but in general the typical line regulation

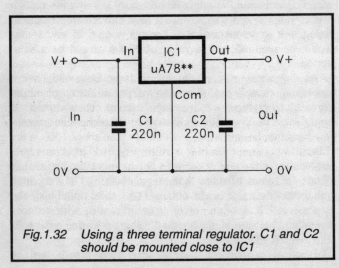

Fig.1.32   Using a three terminal regulator. C1 and C2
           should be mounted close to IC1

48

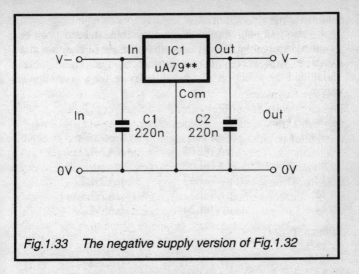

Fig.1.33 *The negative supply version of Fig.1.32*

is better than 0.1%, and load regulation is about 0.25%. The ripple rejection is about 70dB, and the output noise voltage is in the region of 75 microvolts. These figures are more than adequate for most purposes, and the performance of these components is remarkably good considering their very low cost.

All devices in the series feature output overload protection in the form of foldback current limiting. This simply means that in the event of a severe output overload, the output current is not merely prevented from exceeding a figure slightly above the maximum output current of the regulator. Beyond the overload point, attempts to increase the loading on the output actually result in a reduction in the output current. The short circuit output current is generally about 40% of the component's maximum output current rating.

Foldback current limiting reduces the risk of damage to components in the circuit supplied via the regulator, and it also helps to reduce dissipation in the regulator itself. The dissipation in the regulator could otherwise be substantially higher than its normal operating level. The drop-out voltage is two volts for five volt regulators, and 2.5 volts for other types. In other words, the regulator will work properly provided the input voltage is always at least two or 2.5 volts more than the output voltage.

A variety of output voltages are available, and most can be obtained in negative as well as positive versions. They are also available with several output current ratings. These tables should aid the selection of a suitable device for a given application.

100mA Types

Voltage	Positive	Negative
5	µA78L05	µA79L05
8	µA78L08	–
12	µA78L12	µA79L12
15	µA78L15	µA79L15
24	µA78L24	µA79L24

500mA Types

Voltage	Positive	Negative
5	µA78M05	µA79M05
12	µA78M12	µA79M12
15	µA78M15	µA79M15
24	µA78M24	µA79M24

1A Types

Voltage	Positive	Negative
5	µA7805	µA7905
6	µA7806	–
8	µA7808	µA7908
12	µA7812	µA7912
15	µA7815	µA7915
18	µA7818	–
24	µA7824	µA7924

2A Types

Voltage	Positive	Negative
5	µA78S05	–
12	µA78S12	–
15	µA78S15	–
24	µA78S24	–

Leadout details for a range of three terminal monolithic voltage regulators are provided in Figure 1.34.

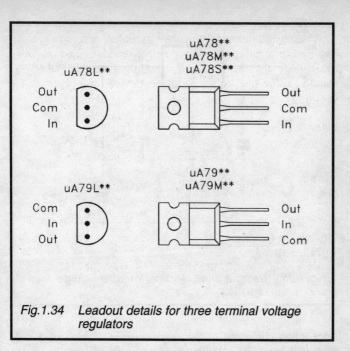

uA78L**

Out
Com
In

uA78**
uA78M**
uA78S**

Out
Com
In

uA79L**

Com
In
Out

uA79**
uA79M**

Out
In
Com

*Fig.1.34   Leadout details for three terminal voltage
regulators*

Variable Voltage

Figure 1.35 shows the circuit diagram for a voltage regulator based on an LM317* series three terminal variable regulator. These are used in much the same way as normal 78** series monolithic voltage regulators, but two discrete resistors enable a wide range of output voltages to be obtained. The basic action of the circuit is to stabilise the output potential at 1.2 volts above the potential at the "Adjust" terminal. R1 and R2 form a potential divider, and their purpose is to take the voltage at the "Adjust" input to 1.2 volts less than the required output voltage.

There is a slight flaw in this setup in that any change in the current consumption of IC1 itself will result in the voltage developed across R1 changing. This would, in turn, alter the output voltage. In practice this is not a major problem because the LM317* series of regulators are designed to operate at a supply current of only about 50 microamps. This is insignifi-

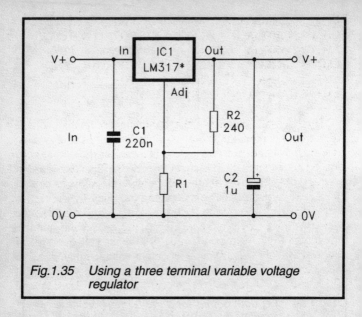

Fig.1.35   Using a three terminal variable voltage regulator

cant when compared to the recommended current of 5 milliamps through the potential divider circuit.

Determining the correct value for R1 is quite easy. The output voltage is equal to 1 volt for every 200 ohms of resistance through R1 and R2. Therefore, simply deducting 1.2 from the required output voltage and then multiplying this value by 200 will give the correct value for R1. Suppose that an output potential of 10 volts is required. Deducting 1.2 volts from 10 volts gives an answer of 8.8 volts. Multiplying 8.8 by 200 gives a value of 1760 ohms, or 1.76k in other words. The nearest preferred value of 1.8k would be used, and would provide a typical output voltage of 10.2 volts. R1 must be a preset resistor in applications that require a very accurate supply voltage. The output potential can then be trimmed to precisely the required figure.

There are four versions of the LM317, and the main differences between them are detailed in this table. This also gives details of the LM338K, which is effectively a higher current version of the LM317K.

Device	Max. Output	Drop-Out V	Case	Max. Power
LM317L	100mA	1.8V	TO92	0.625W
LM317M	500mA	1.8V	TO220	12W
LM317T	1.5A	2.25V	TO220	15W
LM317K	1.5A	2.5V	TO3	20W
LM338K	5A	2.9V	TO3	–

The drop-out voltage is the minimum acceptable voltage drop from the input to the output of the device. In other words, the input voltage must always be higher than the output voltage by an amount which is equal to or higher than the drop-out voltage. Otherwise the output voltage will fall below its correct level. Also, the electronic smoothing provided by the device will be largely lost. With the exception of the LM338K, the output voltage range for all versions is 1.2 to 37 volts, and the maximum input voltage 40 volts. The input voltage range of the LM338K is 4 to 35V, and its output voltage range is 1.2 to 32 volts. The load and line regulation figures are very good at 0.1% and 0.01% respectively for all four types. The line and load regulation figures for the LM338K are 0.005% and 0.1% respectively. Ripple rejection is 80dB (75dB for the LM338K), and the output noise voltage is typically about 150 microvolts for all five devices.

There are negative supply versions of most of the LM317* series, and these are used in essentially the same manner as the LM317* devices. These are the LM337* devices. Figure 1.36 shows the circuit diagram for a three terminal negative supply regulator.

Figure 1.37 provides leadout details for a range of three terminal adjustable voltage regulators.

Zeners

Zener diodes seem to be little used in modern electronic circuits, and have been largely supplanted by integrated circuit voltage regulators. A basic zener stabiliser is a shunt type, and as such it is only suitable for low power applications. In normal use a zener diode would therefore be used to stabilise the supply to a critical part of the circuit, or to provide a stabilised bias voltage to a critical section of the circuit. With many circuits now being powered via highly stable monolithic voltage

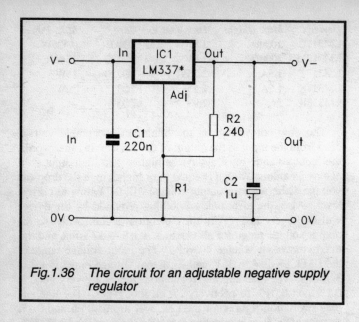

Fig.1.36   The circuit for an adjustable negative supply regulator

regulators, accurate operation of the circuit is often guaranteed without the need for any built-in voltage regulators.

I suppose that zener diodes still have their uses, but it is probably better to use alternatives wherever possible. Zener diodes tend to be less accurate than modern alternatives, and generally provide inferior regulation. Low voltage types having zener voltages of about 6.8 volts or less often provide rather poor regulation.

The circuit diagram for a basic zener regulator is shown in Figure 1.38. C1 is a decoupling capacitor, and its main function is actually to filter out the relatively high noise level produced across a zener diode. The value of load resistor R1 is important as it must always provide an adequate current flow to the output, but it must not be so low in value that large amounts of power are wasted in the zener diode, possibly causing it to burn out.

The basic action of the circuit is for the zener diode to conduct more heavily if the load current decreases, or less heavily if the load current increases. This keeps the overall current

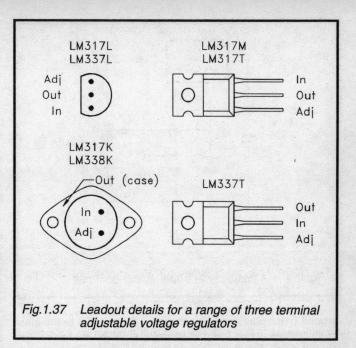

Fig.1.37 *Leadout details for a range of three terminal adjustable voltage regulators*

drain more or less constant, and avoids variations in the output potential due to changes in loading. If the input voltage should increase or decrease for some reason, D1 conducts more or less heavily so that the voltage drop through R1 changes by virtually the same amount. This keeps the output voltage almost unchanged.

In order to calculate the correct value for R1 it is necessary to know the minimum input voltage, the maximum output current, and the output voltage. The output voltage is deducted from the minimum input voltage to give the minimum voltage across R1. For the circuit to stand any chance of working reasonably well this should be at least one volt, and preferably two or three volts. There must always be at least a small current flow through D1 for it to provide a stabilising action, and this current must be added to the output current. For small zener diodes a current of two or three milliamps is usually sufficient, but most types provide optimum efficiency at a current of

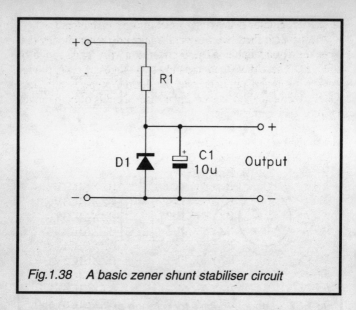

Fig.1.38   A basic zener shunt stabiliser circuit

around five milliamps. The value for R1 is equal to the minimum voltage across this component divided by the total output current (including the zener current).

As a simple example, assume that the minimum input potential will be 8 volts, that the output voltage is 6.2 volts, and that the maximum output current is 7.5 milliamps. This gives a minimum voltage across R1 of 1.8 volts (8V – 6.2V equals 1.8V). Allowing 2.5 milliamps for the minimum zener current, this gives a total output current of 10 milliamps, or 0.01 amps in other words. The correct value for R1 is therefore equal to 1.8 volts divided by 0.01 amps, which gives an answer of 180 ohms. This is a preferred value, but in most cases the calculated value will not precisely coincide with a preferred value. It is then a matter of using the nearest preferred value below the calculated figure.

It is as well to calculate the power dissipated by D1 and R1 under worst case conditions to ensure that these will not be excessive for ordinary 250mW and 400mW components. If necessary, higher power components can then be substituted. However, for medium and high power applications some form of series regulator is generally much more satisfactory.

At one time there were several ranges of zener diodes that were readily available. These covered a very wide range of voltages. These days there are only two ranges of zener diodes stocked by most suppliers, and the 400mW type is now less widely available than was once the case. Details of both ranges are provided in this table.

Voltage	400mW	1.3W
2.7V	BZY88C2V7	–
3V	BZY88C3V0	–
3.3V	BZY88C3V3	BZX61C3V3
3.6V	BZY88C3V6	BZX61C3V6
3.9V	BZY88C3V9	BZX61C3V9
4.3V	BZY88C4V3	BZX61C4V3
4.7V	BZY88C4V7	BZX61C4V7
5.1V	BZY88C5V1	BZX61C5V1
5.6V	BZY88C5V6	BZX61C5V6
6.2V	BZY88C6V2	BZX61C6V2
6.8V	BZY88C6V8	BZX61C6V8
7.5V	BZY88C7V5	BZX61C7V5
8.2V	BZY88C8V2	BZX61C8V2
9.1V	BZY88V9V1	BZX61C9V1
10V	BZY88C10V	BZX61C10V
11V	BZY88C11V	BZX61C11V
12V	BZY88C12V	BZX61C12V
13V	BZY88C13V	BZX61C13V
15V	BZY88C15V	BZX61C15V
16V	BZY88C16V	BZX61C16V
18V	BZY88C18V	BZX61C18V
20V	BZY88C20V	BZX61C20V
24V	BZY88C24V	BZX61C24V
27V	BZY88C27V	BZX61C27V
30V	BZY88C30V	BZX61C30V
33V	BZY88C33V	BZX61C33V
36V	–	BZX61C36V
39V	–	BZX61C39V
43V	–	BZX61C43V
47V	–	BZX6147V

Current Regulators

In some applications it is a stabilised current flow rather than a regulated voltage that is required. There are numerous constant current generator configurations in common use, but for most purposes the very basic configuration of Figure 1.39 will suffice. There are actually two circuits here, but they use what is essentially the same configuration. The circuit on the left uses an n.p.n. transistor and it acts as a current sink. The one on the right is based on a p.n.p. transistor and it acts as a current source. Operation of this type of constant current generator is very straightforward. Here we will consider the current source, but the current sink circuit operates in basically the same fashion.

R1 and the two diodes provide a base voltage to TR1 which is stabilised about 1.3 volts below the positive supply potential. This gives about 0.65 volts or so across emitter resistor R2, and this sets a certain emitter current. With a high gain transistor such as the BC557 specified for TR1, there is little difference between the emitter and collector currents. This gives a current flow in the output circuit that is virtually equal to the emitter current. The required output current can therefore be set by giving R2 a suitable value.

Of course, the circuit only works properly if there is a low enough load resistance across the output. The higher the supply voltage, the higher the load resistance that the circuit can tolerate before it can not drive a high enough current through the load. The maximum output voltage is about 1 volt less than the supply voltage. The maximum supply voltage for the circuit is 30 volts, which is imposed by the collector to emitter voltage rating of the BC557. Using a higher voltage transistor enables correspondingly higher supply voltages to be used, and higher output voltages to be achieved. Practically any silicon p.n.p. transistor can be used in the TR1 position, but the current gain of the device should be about 100 or more.

Calculating the value for R2 is very simple. Dividing 0.65 by the required output current gives the value for R2. For example, suppose an output current of 10 milliamps (0.01 amps) is required. Dividing 0.65 by 0.01 gives a value of 65 ohms for R2. In practice the nearest preferred value of 68 ohms would have to be used. This gives a typical output current of

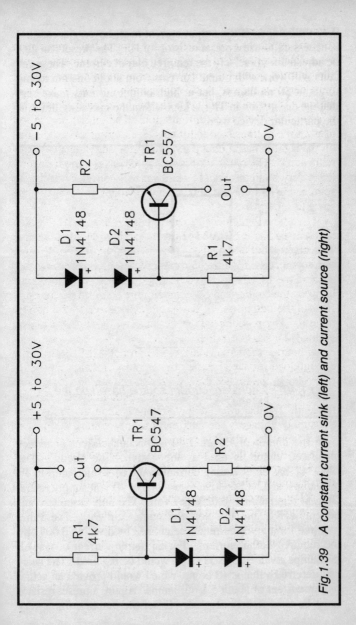

Fig. 1.39 A constant current sink (left) and current source (right)

0.96 milliamps. If the output current must be very accurate it is necessary to use a preset resistor for R2. The preset can then be adjusted for precisely the required output current. These circuits will work with output currents from about one microamp to about 50 milliamps, but at high output currents make sure that the dissipation in TR1 is kept within the operating limits of the particular device used.

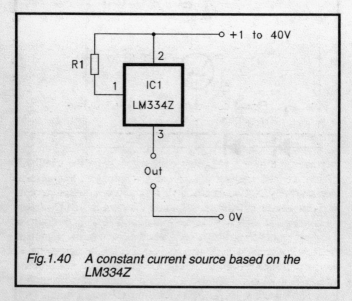

Fig.1.40   A constant current source based on the LM334Z

In the circuit of Figure 1.40 a constant current generator integrated circuit is used as the basis of the circuit. The LM334Z has an operating current range of 1 microamp to 10 milliamps, and will operate over a one to 40 volt supply range. Current regulation is 0.02% per volt. The only discrete component is R1, and this sets the output current. The value required for a given current is calculated by dividing 0.0677 by the required output current. For an output current of (say) 5 milliamps a value of 13.54 ohms would be required. The nearest preferred value is 13 ohms, which would provide an actual output current of about 5.2 milliamps. Again, a preset resistor must be used if it is necessary to set the output current very

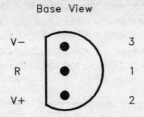

Fig.1.41 *Pinout details for the LM334Z current regulator*

accurately. Figure 1.41 shows leadout details for the LM334Z.

The circuits of Figure 1.39 and 1.40 are not temperature compensated, and will produce slightly reduced output currents with increased ambient temperature. The basic LM334Z current generator suffers from a similar problem. The modified arrangement of Figure 1.42 works in the same basic fashion as the original current sink and source circuits, but gives better temperature stabilisation. However, it requires a well stabilised supply if it is to function well. Temperature compensation is achieved by using just a single diode in the base circuit of TR1. Any change in the base - emitter voltage of TR1 due to a temperature change will produce a similar change in voltage across D1. This leaves the voltage across emitter resistor R3 largely unchanged, and the output current therefore remains virtually the same as well.

Other supply voltages can be used provided the value of R1 (R2 in the current source) is changed to suit, and the supply voltage is kept between 5 and 30 volts. The value of R1 (in kilohms) should be about 1.4 less than the supply potential in volts (e.g. 4k7 for a 6 volt supply).

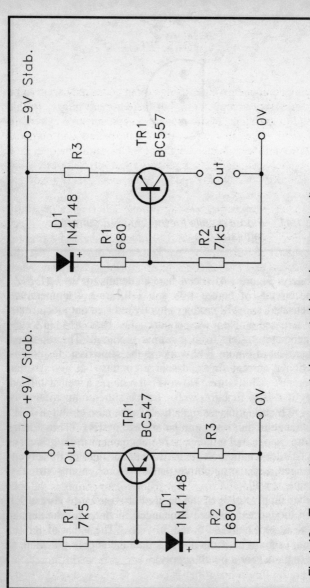

Fig. 1.42 Temperature compensated current sink and source circuits

Chapter 2

CODES, ETC.

Marking component values using colour codes may seem to be an unnecessary complication, but there are advantages to this method of marking. Many modern components are extremely small, and values marked on them using letters and numbers would require a character height of under a millimetre. Few people could read the values reliably (if at all) without the aid of a magnifier. Coloured bands or spots, even if very small, are relatively easy to read.

Another problem with using minute lettering is that only minor damage is sufficient to render the value completely illegible. Even with severe wear, the coloured bands of a resistor colour code can usually be read with little difficulty. For the experienced user colour codes have a further advantage. Most values can be recognised "on sight", and there is no need to do any calculating of values. This makes it easy to pick out a component of the required value from a box of assorted values. The same is not true if the values are simply marked using letters and numbers. It is then necessary to read the values of the components, one-by-one, until you find one having the correct value.

Resistor Codes

At present the only large scale use of colour codes is for marking the values and tolerance ratings of resistors. These codes do crop up on a few other types of component though, such as capacitors and inductors. Here we will consider all three types of component, starting with resistors.

The most common form of resistor colour coding is the four band variety. Details of this method are shown in Figure 2.1. The first task with any resistor colour code is to identify the first band in the code. In the past the first band was the one nearest to one end of the body. This method does not seem to be reliable when applied to modern resistors, and it may actually be the fourth band that is closest to one end of the body. Fortunately there is a much more reliable method, which is

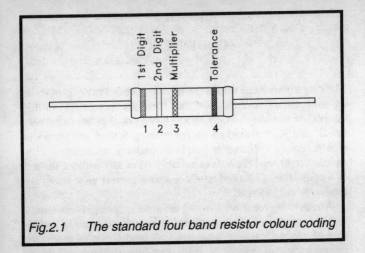

Fig.2.1   The standard four band resistor colour coding

based on the spacing between bands. The first, second, and third bands should be spaced quite closely, with the fourth band well separated from this main group. With many practical resistors the fourth band is either gold or silver in colour, which is not a colour that is used for band one. The correct reading order for the bands is then immediately obvious.

This table shows the significance of each colour in each of the four bands.

COLOUR	BAND 1	BAND 2	BAND 3	BAND 4
Black	0	0	×1	–
Brown	1	1	×10	1%
Red	2	2	×100	2%
Orange	3	3	×1000	–
Yellow	4	4	×10000	–
Green	5	5	×100000	0.5%
Blue	6	6	×1000000	0.25%
Violet	7	7	–	0.1%
Grey	8	8	–	–
White	9	9	–	–
Gold	–	–	×0.1	5%
Silver	–	–	×0.01	10%
None	–	–	–	20%

If we take a couple of examples to demonstrate how the system operates, a resistor with the colour coding brown – black – orange – gold would have a value of 10k, and a tolerance of plus and minus 5%. The brown band indicates that the first digit of the value is "1", while the black band indicates that the second digit is "0". This gives "10", which is multiplied by 1000, as indicated by the orange third band. 10 multiplied by 1000 is obviously 10000, which is the value in ohms. A value as high as this would more normally be expressed in kilohms, which gives a value of 10k.

A convenient way of handling the multiplier is to take its band one value, and then add that many zeros to the first two digits. In this example the multiplier is orange, which indicates a value of three if it occurs as the first band. Adding three zeros to the first two digits of the value ("10" plus "000") again gives a value of 10000 ohms, or 10k. This simple dodge does not work properly if the third band is silver or gold, as these colours are not used for band one.

The fourth band is gold, and this indicates a tolerance of plus and minus 5%. In other words, the actual value of the component is within five percent of its marked value. In our 10k example, this means that the real value of the component will be between 9.5k and 10.5k.

As an example of a low value, consider the code red – red – gold – gold. The first two digits of the value are clearly "2" and "2". The third band is gold, which indicates that multiplication by 0.1 is required. Multiplying 22 by 0.1 obviously gives a value of 2.2 ohms. The fourth band is gold, which again indicates a tolerance of plus and minus five percent.

Five Band Codes
The four band method of coding is satisfactory for values in the normal E12 and E24 series of preferred values, but is unable to accommodate some of the odd values sometimes used in industrial electronics. A five band coding is used for these awkward values, and resistors supplied to amateur users are sometimes marked with these five band codes. Figure 2.2 shows the way in which this method of five band coding operates, and it has clear similarities with the four band method. In fact the first two and last two bands have the same functions as the bands

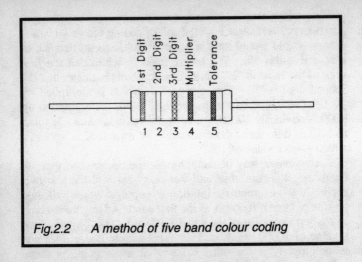

1st Digit
2nd Digit
3rd Digit
Multiplier
Tolerance

1 2 3 4 5

Fig.2.2   A method of five band colour coding

in the normal four colour system. An extra band is grafted into
the middle of the code in order to permit values to be marked
more precisely.

If we take a simple example, a coding of red – white –
green – red – brown would indicate a value of 29.5k and a
tolerance of plus and minus one percent. The first three bands
give the first three digits of the value, which in this case are
"295". The fourth band is the multiplier, and a red band
indicates that the first three digits must be multiplied by 100.
This gives a total value of 29500 ohms (295 multiplied by 100
equals 29500), or 29.5k in other words. The fifth band is
brown, which indicates a tolerance of plus and minus one
percent.

As component retailers only sell resistors which have
normal preferred values, the extra band does not really fulfil
any useful purpose as far as amateur users are concerned. Any
resistors you buy which use this method of coding will almost
certainly have a black third band. For example, a 39k two
percent tolerance resistor would have the colour code orange –
white – black – red – red. You can therefore calculate the value
by ignoring the third band, and using a multiplier ten times
higher than indicated by the fourth band.

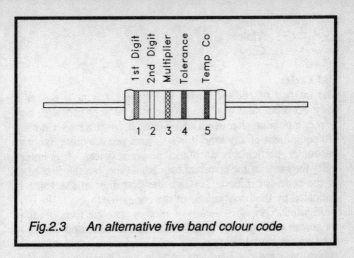

Fig.2.3   An alternative five band colour code

There is an alternative form of five band resistor code, and
details of this code are provided in Figure 2.3. Having two different five band codes is obviously a bit unfortunate, and it is
essential to look carefully at any five band code in order to
ascertain which particular type it is. If in doubt, the value of
the resistor can only be determined for certain by measuring it
using a multimeter.

This second five band coding is very straightforward, and is
essentially the same as the normal four band variety. The first
four bands indicate the value and tolerance rating using the
standard four band method of coding. The fifth band indicates
the temperature coefficient of the component. This is something that is not normally of any great importance, and a components list is unlikely to specify this parameter. Anyway, for
the record, this is a list of the colours and their respective
temperature coefficients.

Colour	Temp. Co. (ppm/degree C)
Black	200
Brown	100
Red	50
Orange	25
Yellow	15

Blue	10
Violet	5
Grey	1

Old Codes

The method of coding shown in Figure 2.4 is now well and truly obsolete, and you are unlikely to be supplied with any new components that use it. However, it you are into restoring old equipment of any kind it is a system you are quite likely to encounter, particularly on higher power resistors. It is essentially the same as the standard four band type, but the first band of the code is omitted. Instead, the first digit of the value is indicated by the body colour of the component.

Figure 2.5 provides details of another obsolete form of resistor colour coding. As far as I am aware, this method was only used on resistors having power ratings of a few watts of more. Again, you are not likely to be sold new components which have this method of colour coding, but resistors of this type are quite likely to be encountered by anyone undertaking repair or restoration work on old equipment. Also, resistors having old methods of coding sometimes turn up in bargain packs of components. The value is indicated in a fashion which is based on the normal four band method of coding. No tolerance rating is indicated by this method of coding.

It has to be pointed out that not all resistors have their values marked using a colour code. This system is used for the vast majority of small resistors, but is little used for larger types having power ratings of more than about 2 watts. The value is generally marked on larger resistors in the same form that the value would be printed on a circuit diagram. For example, values of 2.2k and 0.33 ohms would be marked as "2k2" and "0R33" respectively. The tolerance is sometimes marked using a code letter, as detailed in the table shown on page 70.

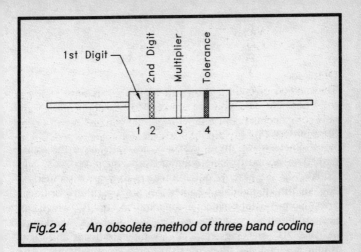

Fig.2.4   An obsolete method of three band coding

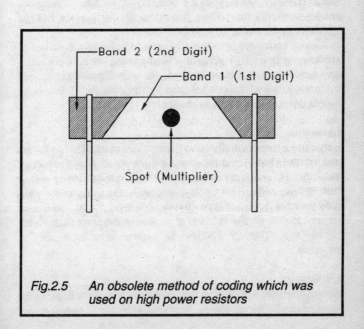

Fig.2.5   An obsolete method of coding which was
           used on high power resistors

Code Letter	Tolerance
F	1%
G	2%
H	2.5%
J	5%
K	10%
M	20%

Potentiometers

Potentiometers and preset resistors normally have the value marked in normal circuit diagram form, such as "4k7" and "220k". In the case of potentiometers they are also marked "log" or "lin" to indicate whether they are logarithmic or linear types. Some potentiometers are marked "A" or "B", which can be in addition to or instead of the "log" and "lin" markings. "A" and "B" markings respectively indicate linear and logarithmic components. Preset resistors do not normally have any form of marking to indicate whether they are logarithmic or linear, but only linear types are generally available. Tolerances are not normally marked on potentiometers or presets, but the tolerance is normally 20% in both cases.

Colour codes are occasionally used to indicate the values of preset resistors. This generally works using what is basically the standard resistor code method, but with the value indicated by three coloured dots rather than by three bands. There is no fourth dot to indicate the tolerance.

Inductors

Large inductors normally have their values marked using letters and figures, but it is quite common for small high frequency inductors (r.f. chokes) to have the value marked using a four band colour code. This coding is actually the same as the standard four band resistor type, giving both a value and a tolerance rating. However, the value is in nanohenries rather than ohms. Divide the value by 1000 if an answer in microhenries is required.

Capacitors

Some years ago it was quite common for capacitors to be marked with colour codes, but relatively few capacitors are colour coded these days. At one time virtually all the C280 style plastic foil capacitors were colour coded, but this method of value marking is one that is only encountered infrequently at present. Figure 2.6 shows how the C280 method of coding operates. Once again, the method used is firmly based on the standard four band resistor coding. The first three bands indicate the value in normal resistor fashion, but the value is in picofarads. To convert this into a value nanofarads it is merely necessary to divide by 1000. Divide the marked value by 1000000 if a value in microfarads is required.

The fourth band indicates the tolerance, but the colour coding used is different to the resistor equivalent. The fifth band shows the maximum working voltage of the component. Details of the fourth and fifth band colour coding is provided in this table.

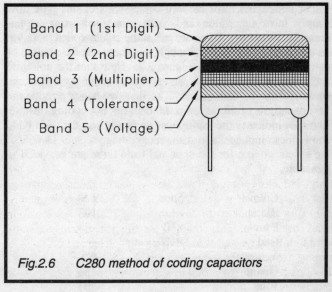

Fig.2.6   C280 method of coding capacitors

Colour	Band 4	Band 5
Black	20%	–
White	10%	–
Green	5%	–

Orange	2.5%	–
Red	2%	250V
Brown	1%	–
Yellow	–	400V

Most of the C280 style capacitors you obtain are likely to be 250 volt types, but 400 volt types are sold by some retailers. Values of 220n or less generally have a tolerance of 20 percent, with higher values having a tolerance of 10 percent. A component having the colour code orange – orange – yellow – white – red would have a value of 330n (330000p), a tolerance of 10 percent, and a maximum operating voltage of 250 volts.

Tantalum Bead

At one time practically all tantalum bead capacitors carried colour codes, but most modern components of this type now simply have the value and voltage marked using alphanumeric characters. There are still some colour coded tantalum components in circulation though, and these use the method of colour coding detailed in Figure 2.7. Note that the coloured spot is the multiplier colour, and also enables the polarity of the component to be determined. The first two bands provide the first two digits of the value in standard resistor coding fashion. The spot indicates the multiplication factor, and the third band shows the component's maximum operating voltage. Details of the colour coding for the spot and band three are provided in this table.

Colour	Spot	Band 3
Black	×1	10V
Brown	×10	–
Red	×100	–
Yellow	–	6.3V
Green	–	16V
Blue	–	20V
Grey	×0.01	25V
White	×0.1	25V
Pink	–	3V

The multiplier coding is much the same as for resistor coding, but most multiplier values are unused because these capacitors are not manufactured in high enough values. Note that, unlike the C280 system, the value is in microfarads and not picofarads.

Ceramic Capacitors

Colour coding on ceramic capacitors was never universal, and it is now extremely rare. Figure 2.8 shows two methods of colour coding for components of this type, but except when dealing with older equipment, you are unlikely to encounter either of them. Coloured spots rather than bands are used, but in other respects the system operates in the same fashion as standard four band resistor colour coding. The values are in picofarads incidentally.

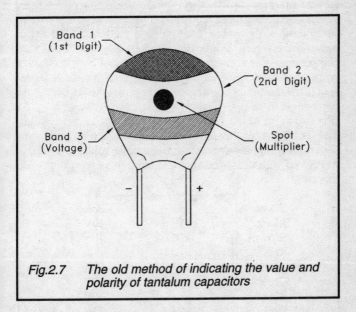

Fig.2.7   The old method of indicating the value and polarity of tantalum capacitors

Other Codes

Although most capacitors are now marked with their values, etc. using alpha-numeric characters, the values are sometimes in slightly cryptic forms. Ceramic and certain other capacitors are often marked with a three figure code, such as "104". The first two figures are the first two digits of the value, and the third digit is the multiplier. Simply add the number of zeros indicated by the third digit. In our example the first two digits are "10", and four zeros must be added to them. This gives a total value of 100000 picofarads, which is the same as 100 nanofarads, or 0.1 microfarads.

The tolerance is sometimes marked using a code letter. This operates using the method of resistor coding that was described previously (e.g. "H" indicates a tolerance of 2.5 percent).

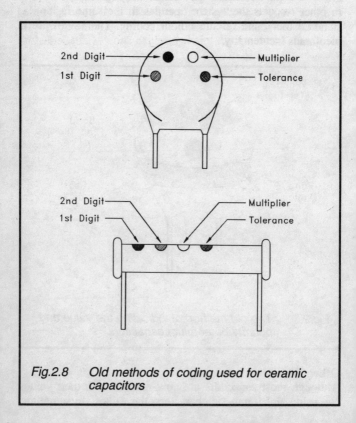

Fig.2.8   Old methods of coding used for ceramic capacitors

Ceramic plate capacitors often have rather odd looking value markings. The low values are usually easy to decipher, with markings such as "33p" and "2p2". It is values from 100p to 820p that can look a little strange. Value markings such as "n1" and "n47" are often encountered. These value markings are in what is basically just the normal circuit diagram form, but with the leading zero omitted. Thus, a capacitor marked "n33" has a value of 0.33n, or 330p in other words.

Preferred Values
Resistors, capacitors, and inductors are manufactured in a range of standard values. There are actually two ranges of values in common use, called the "E12" and "E24" series. These are basically the same, but the "E24" series has some extra values, as can be seen from this list, which shows both series of values.

E12	E24
1.0	1.0
–	1.1
1.2	1.2
–	1.3
1.5	1.5
–	1.6
1.8	1.8
–	2.0
2.2	2.2
–	2.4
2.7	2.7
–	3.0
3.3	3.3
–	3.6
3.9	3.9
–	4.3
4.7	4.7
–	5.1
5.6	5.6
–	6.2
6.8	6.8
–	7.5
8.2	8.2
–	9.1

Although this list would tend to suggest that only values from 1 ohm to 9.1 ohms (or whatever) are available, the same values but in different decades are also available. For example, values such as 100 ohms, 110 ohms, 120 ohms, 130 ohms, etc., can be obtained. The highest resistance value available from most component retailers is 10 megohms, but higher value resistors are manufactured. At the other end of the range there are components having values in the sub one ohm decades, such as 0.1 ohms, 0.11 ohms, 0.12 ohms, 0.13 ohms, etc. Most electronic component retailers only supply values down to one ohm, but some retailers stock lower values, especially in the higher power ratings. However, the range of values available may be rather limited. Capacitors are available over a range of values from about 1p to around 22000µ. Inductors are available in values from about 0.22µH to around 10H.

Chapter 3

OPERATIONAL AMPLIFIERS

Operational amplifiers are undoubtedly the most popular form of linear integrated circuit at present, and seem likely to remain so for many years to come. They were originally designed for use in analogue computers where they performed mathematical operations. It is from this that the "operational" part of the name is derived. These days analogue computers are virtually extinct, but operational amplifiers live on in a wide range of applications including test gear, audio equipment, motor control, and robotics.

A slightly unusual aspect of these components is their power supply requirements. They are designed for use with dual balanced supplies that would normally be about plus and minus 12 to 15 volts. The earth rail is a central 0 volt type. The reason for using dual supplies is that in analogue computing applications it is essential for the amplifier to be able to handle positive and negative output voltages. The output voltage represents the answer to a calculation, and it is essential that positive and negative quantities can both be represented.

It is still quite common for circuits using these devices to have dual supply rails, even though they are little used in analogue computing. There can be advantages to using dual supply rails, and they remain essential in some d.c. applications. However, it is probable that the majority of operational amplifier based circuits now use a single supply. This is perfectly satisfactory in audio and other a.c. applications where normal biasing techniques can be used to permit single supply operation. It is also permissible in d.c. applications where negative output voltages are not required, but only if the operational amplifiers used are intended for single supply use. The LM324N, LM1458C, CA3130E and CA3140E are probably the best known devices of this type.

Inverting Mode
An operational amplifier has two inputs, which are the inverting (–) and non-inverting (+) inputs. It is a form of differential

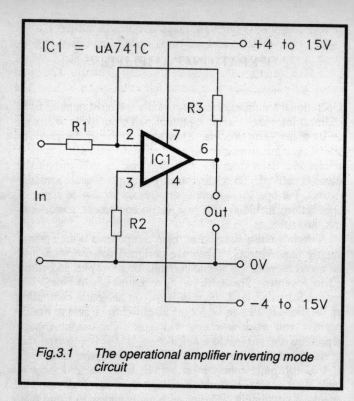

Fig.3.1 The operational amplifier inverting mode circuit

amplifier, with the output voltage reflecting the difference between the two input voltages. However, in normal use operational amplifiers are in circuits that provide straightforward amplification of a single input signal. For general amplification purposes operational amplifiers are an attractive choice as they enable the voltage gain and input impedance to be set very accurately using some fundamental mathematics. Operational amplifiers can be used in two basic amplifying modes, which are the inverting and non-inverting types.

Figure 3.1 shows the circuit diagram for an operational amplifier used in the inverting mode. This requires only two resistors to set the voltage gain and input impedance of the circuit. As the name of this mode suggests, the signal is phase shifted by 180 degrees between the input and output of this circuit. This will often be of no practical consequence, but it is a factor that must be borne in mind when using this configuration in applications where signal phasing is important.

R1 and R3 form the negative feedback network. The input resistance/impedance is equal to the value given to R1. The voltage gain is equal to R3/R1. Thus, in order to obtain a certain combination of input impedance and voltage gain it is merely necessary to give R1 a value which is equal to the required input impedance. R3 is then give a value which is equal to the value of R1 multiplied by the required voltage gain. This is the theory at any rate.

Gain-Bandwidth

In practice it is necessary to bear in mind that "real world" operational amplifiers do not achieve theoretical perfection. A theoretical operational amplifier has infinite innate voltage gain. The innate voltage gain is termed the "open-loop" voltage gain. The voltage gain of the circuit as a whole is called the "closed-loop" voltage gain. A theoretical operational amplifier also has an infinite bandwidth and no input capacitance.

In general, the voltage gain of an operational amplifier is very high at d.c., and is typically about 200000 times. However, in order to avoid problems with instability the high frequency response of the amplifier is rolled-off at 6dB per octave. As already pointed out, operational amplifiers were originally designed for use at d.c., and in this context high frequency roll-off generally means attenuating frequencies above about 10Hz! The graph of Figure 3.2 shows the open-loop frequency response for the industry standard μA741C operational amplifier. The voltage gain set by the feedback network can only be maintained at frequencies where the required closed-loop gain is higher than the open-loop gain.

The unity gain/bandwidth product is an extremely important parameter when using operational amplifiers in a.c. applications. This is the frequency at which the open-loop voltage gain falls to unity, and for the μA741C it is 1MHz, as can be seen from Figure 3.2. With the usual 6dB per octave attenuation rate this makes it easy to calculate the bandwidth for various closed-loop voltage gains. It is just a matter of dividing

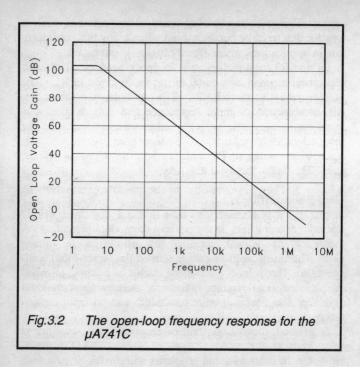

Fig.3.2   The open-loop frequency response for the
μA741C

1000000 by the closed loop voltage gain. For example, at a
closed-loop gain of five the uA741C will have a bandwidth of
200kHz (1000000/5 = 200000Hz or 200kHz).

It is apparent from this that normal operational amplifiers
are not suitable for applications where both high gain and wide
bandwidth are required. More modern types often have significantly higher gain bandwidth products than the μA741C, with
figure of around 3 to 5MHz being typical. A few have gain
bandwidth products as high as 10MHz, but they are still primarily intended for audio use, offering a gain of 500 at the
highest audio frequency of 20kHz. This compares to a maximum gain of just 50 for the μA741C at the same frequency.
There are now a few special types that have gain bandwidth
products of around 100MHz, and which are suitable for use
with video signals, etc., but these are relatively expensive.
They also need carefully designed component layouts in order

to obtain stable operation.

A combination of high input impedance and even moderate voltage gain is something that is beyond the capabilities of the inverting mode. One problem is that R3 must have an impractically high value for such a combination. An input impedance of one megohm and a voltage gain of 100 would require a value of 100M! The other main problem is that of stray capacitances in the circuit, especially the input capacitance of the operational amplifier itself. The input capacitance is usually only a few picofarads, but can be rather more than this with some f.e.t. input types. Even so, with very high value feedback resistors it is likely that large irregularities in the frequency response will be produced, especially at high frequencies. Where high gain and high impedance are required it is necessary to use a low gain input stage followed by one or two higher gain stages.

It is not essential to include R2, and the non-inverting input of IC1 can be connected direct to the 0 volt earth rail. Including R2 gives improved accuracy with some operational amplifiers, such as the μA741C, which have relatively high input currents. With low input current devices, especially f.e.t. input types, including R2 is likely to have little or no apparent effect on accuracy. The correct value for R2 is given by this formula:

$$R2 = (R1 \times R3)/R1 + R3$$

Non-Inverting Mode
The other form of amplifier is the non-inverting type. The circuit for an amplifier of this type is shown in Figure 3.3. This mode provides zero phase shift between the input and the output. R2 sets the input resistance of the circuit, and this is again equal to the value of the resistor used here. At low frequencies the input impedance will also be virtually equal to the value of R2. At higher frequencies the input capacitance of IC1, plus other stray circuit capacitances, will shunt R2 and reduce the input impedance. It is possible that the input resistance of the amplifier could significantly reduce the input resistance of the circuit if a very high value is used for R2. However, in practice the input resistance of an operational amplifier is extremely high, particularly once feedback has been applied. A f.e.t. input operational amplifier offers a typical

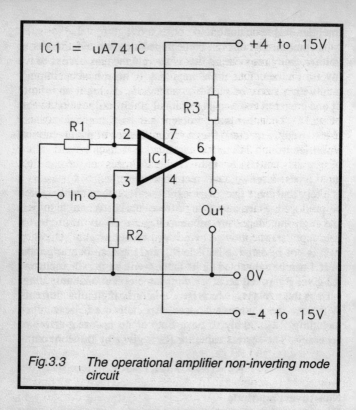

Fig.3.3   The operational amplifier non-inverting mode
            circuit

input resistance of around one million megohms, and will
avoid any significant shunting of R2.

R1 and R3 form the negative feedback network which sets
the closed-loop voltage gain of the circuit. The formula for the
voltage gain of a non-inverting circuit is slightly different to
that for an inverting mode amplifier. The voltage gain is given
by this formula:

$$V \text{ gain} = (R1 + R3)/R1$$

Alternatively, the voltage gain can be calculated by dividing
R3 by R1, and then adding one to the answer. When selecting
suitable values it is a matter of first selecting a suitable value

for R3. This resistor should not be too high in value, or stray capacitances might give problems with peaks and troughs in the frequency response. A very low value would put excessive loading on the output of the amplifier. A theoretical operational amplifier has zero output impedance and can supply an infinite output current. Practical operational amplifiers have quite low output impedances once feedback has been applied, but can usually supply no more than a few milliamps of output current. Values of around 2k2 to 10k are usually satisfactory, and values of up to about 100k or so are usable if flatness of the high frequency response is not of great importance.

Dividing the value of R3 by one less than the required closed-loop voltage gain then provides the correct value for R1. For instance, suppose that a voltage gain of 15 times is required, and the value of R3 has been set at 3k3. Dividing 3300 ohms by 14 gives an answer of 236 ohms. In practice the nearest preferred value of 240 ohms would have to be used, and this would give a typical voltage gain of 14.75. In most applications this is accurate enough, but in critical circuits either R1 or R3 must be a preset resistor so that the gain can be trimmed to precisely the required figure. For a unity voltage gain buffer amplifier the output is simply connected direct to the inverting input, and R1 and R3 are omitted.

Although the non-inverting mode may seem to offer better prospects for a combination of high gain and high input impedance, matters are not that simple. There is no difficulty in selecting values to give something like a 2.2 megohm input impedance and a voltage gain of 200. However, such a combination is likely to give problems with instability due to stray feedback. Such a combination of voltage gain and input impedance is possible, but great care are required with the component layout and wiring. It is easier to obtain good stability using a high input impedance buffer stage followed by a separate amplifier to provide the voltage gain.

Compensation

Most operational amplifiers, including the standard 741C, are fully internally compensated. This simply means that they have an internal capacitor which provides the all-important high frequency roll-off. The main reason for using this roll-off is that stray capacitances can result in large phase shifts through the negative feedback circuit at high frequencies. These phase shifts can be large enough to produce oscillation at high frequencies. Surprisingly perhaps, the lower the closed loop voltage gain of the amplifier, the greater the risk of oscillation occurring.

A fully internally compensated operational amplifier can be used at voltage gains of unity or above without oscillation occurring due to positive feedback via the negative feedback circuit. Of course, if fully compensated devices are used in a high gain circuit which has a poorly designed layout, oscillation may still occur because of stray feedback. Provided they are used sensibly though, fully compensated operational amplifiers should remain stable.

For most purposes fully internally compensated devices are entirely satisfactory. However, they are less than ideal when it is necessary to obtain a high level of voltage gain from a single operational amplifier. As pointed out previously, the gain bandwidth product of most operational amplifiers is not particularly great. Using a lesser degree of high frequency roll-off would give a higher gain bandwidth product, but would not result in oscillation provided the amplifier was used at high voltage gains. This is possible using externally compensated operational amplifiers. These have no internal roll-off capacitor. Instead they are used with a discrete capacitor of appropriate value for the closed loop voltage gain of the circuit.

The 748C is the externally compensated version of the 741C. This requires an external compensation capacitor connected between pins 1 and 8 (pins 3 and 12 for the 14 pin d.i.l. version). The device is fully compensated using a 30p capacitor, and in normal use it would obviously be used with a lower value capacitor in order to obtain increased bandwidth. Figure 3.4 shows the open loop voltage gain of the 748C when it is used with a 30p compensation capacitor at unity voltage gain, and a 2p compensation capacitor at a gain of 100 times. It will be seen from this that a roughly tenfold increase in bandwidth is obtained using the 2p compensation capacitor. This permits an amplifier having a closed loop gain of 100 times to achieve a bandwidth of 100kHz, which is rather more useful than the 10kHz bandwidth obtained from an equivalent amplifier based

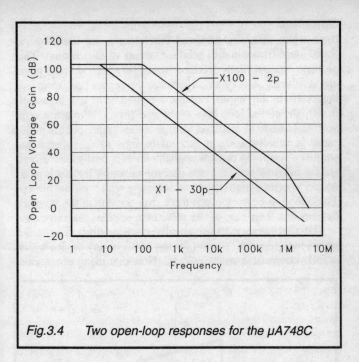

Fig.3.4   Two open-loop responses for the µA748C

on the 741C.

A useful side-effect of using external compensation is that it also gives improved power bandwidth and slew rate ratings. The 741C has a slew rate of only 0.5V per microsecond, but at a voltage gain of 10 times (20dB) the 748C can achieve a slew rate of 5.5 volts per microsecond. The full power bandwidth of the 748C can also be over ten times that of the 741C.

Some operational amplifiers have partial internal compensation. This simply means that they have an internal compensation capacitor, but it does not provide sufficient roll-off to ensure stable operation down to unity voltage gain. Devices of this type have to be used at voltage gains of about five or more, but the exact figure varies somewhat from one type to another. As a practical example, the NE5534AN is internally compensated for voltage gains of more than three, but requires an external compensation capacitor for lower closed loop gains.

Offset Null

Even when carefully designed bias circuits are used, operational amplifiers can still produce output voltage errors. This problem is most likely to occur when very high voltage gains are involved. A very small error at the inputs can become a huge error at the output, because the input error will be amplified by the closed loop gain of the amplifier. There are several potential causes of an offset voltage at the output, but the major cause is usually a slight lack of balance in the operational amplifier itself. In critical applications it is best to use a high quality instrumentation grade operational amplifier that is guaranteed to offer a high degree of accuracy, with minimal offsets. These tend to be very much more expensive than the standard devices, but their ease of use more than justifies the extra cost.

The alternative is to use an offset null control. Figure 3.5 shows the offset null control for the 741C, or any device which is fully compatible with the 741C. Note that many operational

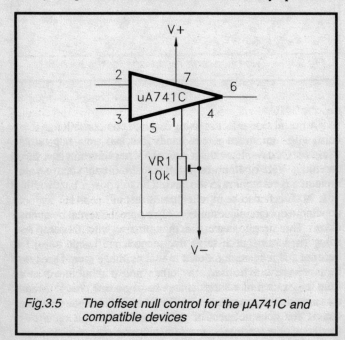

Fig.3.5   The offset null control for the µA741C and
compatible devices

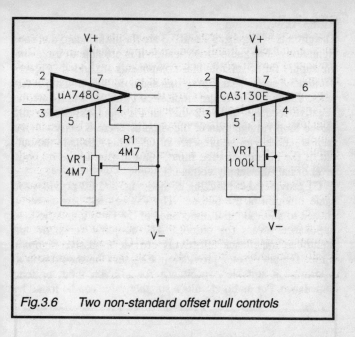

Fig.3.6   Two non-standard offset null controls

amplifiers are not fully compatible with the 741C, and require a different value for VR1, or even have a totally different offset null arrangement. Figure 3.6 shows the circuit for two non-standard offset null controls. Ideally VR1 should be a multi-turn preset potentiometer, but it is usually possible to obtain good results with an ordinary type if it is adjusted very carefully. VR1 is simply adjusted for zero output voltage with no input signal applied to the circuit.

It is only fair to point out that offset null controls are not popular with circuit designers. They are believed by many circuit designers to have a drift problem, with frequent re-adjustment being necessary. My experience would seem to bear out this reputation for drift problems, and it would seem to be more practical to have the offset null potentiometer as a front panel control rather than a preset potentiometer tucked away inside the equipment. Where possible it is better to use a circuit that does not need an offset null control, even if this means using a much more expensive operational amplifier.

Audio Amplification

The circuits of Figures 3.1 and 3.3 are for the standard d.c. configurations. For audio amplification it is possible to use a single supply rail if suitable bias components are added. Figures 3.7 and 3.8 show the a.c. inverting and non-inverting mode circuits. Taking the inverting mode circuit first, R1 and R4 are the negative feedback network that set the input impedance and closed-loop voltage gain of the circuit. There is unity voltage gain at d.c. due to the presence of C1. This results in the output of the circuit, like the input, being biased to the required level of half the supply voltage.

C1 provides d.c. blocking at the input, and C3 provides the same function at the output. The values used here must be chosen to suit the input impedance of the circuit, and the load impedance across the output. The coupling capacitor and input/load impedance effectively provide a passive highpass filter. The tables, etc., provided in Chapter One should help to determine a suitable capacitance for a given input or load impedance. For audio circuits a suitable value can be found by

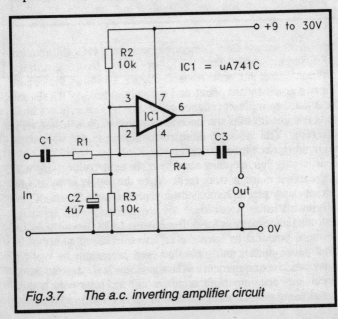

Fig.3.7   The a.c. inverting amplifier circuit

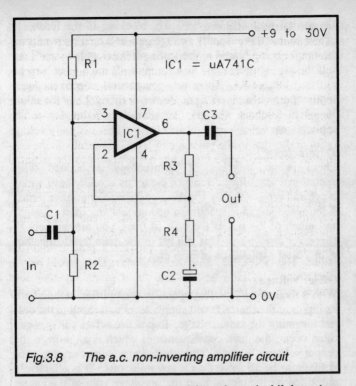

Fig.3.8   The a.c. non-inverting amplifier circuit

dividing 22 by the input or load impedance in kilohms (e.g. 2.2µ for an input impedance of 10k).

R2 and R3 bias the non-inverting input to half the supply voltage. The value of these two resistors is not critical, and anything from a few kilohms to 100k or so should give good results. Of course, they must have the same value. C2 simply decouples noise or stray feedback on the supply lines, and prevents stray pick up at the non-inverting input. Again, its value is not critical.

The non-inverting amplifier has the input biased to half the supply potential by R1 and R2. These set the input impedance of the amplifier, and the value used here must be twice the required input impedance. C1 and C3 provide d.c. blocking at the input and output of the circuit. R3 and R4 are the negative feedback network which control the closed-loop voltage gain in the normal way. C2 provides d.c. blocking in the feedback circuit so that there is unity voltage gain at d.c. This results in the output being biased to the same potential as the input (i.e. half the supply potential). The value of C2 must be chosen to suit the value of R4. These two components effectively form another passive highpass filter. Again, dividing 22 by the value of R4 in kilohms will give a satisfactory value for audio applications.

Terminology
There is no shortage of terminology associated with operational amplifiers. Some of the terms actually have wider usage and are not strictly speaking operational amplifier terms. A lot of the jargon is specific to operational amplifiers though, and much of the rest is the type of thing you are unlikely to encounter elsewhere. This is a list of the main terms, together with a brief explanation of each one.

Offset Voltage
With a theoretically perfect operational amplifier, setting both its inputs at the central 0 volt supply level will result in the output assuming the same voltage. In practice offset voltages can often occur, the main consequence of which is an error in the output voltage. With a closed loop voltage gain of one the error is likely to be no more than a few millivolts. It is effectively amplified by the closed loop (d.c.) voltage gain of the circuit though, and at high gains the error can reach about one volt or even more. Where output errors caused by input offset voltages would otherwise be large enough to cause a malfunction of the circuit, an offset null control can be fitted, as explained previously. Special precision operational amplifiers which have very low offset voltages can be obtained, and generally offer a better solution.

Slew Rate
The slew rate of an operational amplifier (or any other circuit) is the maximum rate at which the output voltage can change. It is usually expressed as a change of so many volts per microsecond. It is an important factor with operational amplifiers that will be used at high frequencies, and by high frequencies I mean the upper end of the audio range or higher. The

frequency response figures of operational amplifiers tend to be a little flattering. They often suggest that a component is perfectly usable at frequencies of a few hundred kilohertz or higher provided only low to moderate voltage gains are required. This may well be the case provided only small signal levels are involved. If large output voltage swings are required, the slew rate might prevent suitably large signals being produced. This is known as "slewing induced distortion", or just "SID" for short. Most modern operational amplifiers have much better slew rates than the early devices, and are very much less prone to this problem. Special high slew rate devices are available.

Large Signal Bandwidth
The large signal bandwidth is similar to slew rate, and is really just a different way of looking at things. It is the maximum frequency at which the amplifier can provide its maximum output voltage swing.

Common Mode Rejection
As an operational amplifier amplifies the voltage difference across its inputs, with a signal applied to both inputs there should be no change in the output voltage. In practice there will be a small imbalance, and some breakthrough at the output will occur. This parameter indicates how well a common input signal is suppressed at the output.

Latch-Up
Ideally, an operational amplifier would operate properly with its inputs at any voltages. Being more realistic, it should ideally operate properly with its inputs at any voltages within the supply levels. Practical devices sometimes fail to achieve this, and will only operate properly if the input voltages are within certain limits, and (or) the differential input voltage does not exceed a certain amount. Taking the input voltages outside the specified operating range is unlikely to result in any damage, provided these voltages are not outside the supply limits. The output of the amplifier will go fully positive or negative though, and may tend to stay in that state even if the input voltages are brought back within the acceptable limits. Switching off, waiting a few seconds, and then switching on again will usually restore normal operation. This "latch-up" as it is called,

is not normally too much of a problem when an operational amplifier is used in one of its standard amplifying modes, but it is a point that has to be kept in mind if it is used as a voltage comparator, or in some unusual circuit configuration.

Output Voltage Swing
The output voltage swing is the maximum positive and negative output levels that can be produced from a given supply voltage. This parameter is often specified with zero load on the output, but it may be given for a particular load impedance. Some modern devices can provide an output voltage swing virtually equal to the supply voltages. In particular, devices intended for operation using a single supply rail can provide output levels at virtually zero volts. With many devices the total output voltage swing is several volts less than the sum of the supply voltages. The standard µA741C type falls within this category.

Output Resistance
A theoretical operational amplifier has zero output resistance, but obviously this is something that is not achievable in practice. Typically the output resistance is quite low at about 75 ohms, and the application of negative feedback in a practical amplifier circuit can produce a closed loop output resistance of about one ohm. This could give the impression that operational amplifiers are power devices capable of providing quite high output currents. Apart from a few special types, this is not the case. Although the output impedance is quite low, and loading effects will normally reduce the output level by only a small amount, this only holds good for low to medium output levels, or for fairly high load impedances. At high signal levels with a low impedance load the output current limiting will come into action, and the output signal will be clipped.

Real Devices
Although operational amplifiers were originally designed for use in analogue computers, they are now used in a wide range of applications, and most practical devices are designed to suit a particular type of circuit (precision d.c., low noise and distortion audio, etc.). This list gives some basic information for a wide range of operational amplifiers, and should prove helpful,

92

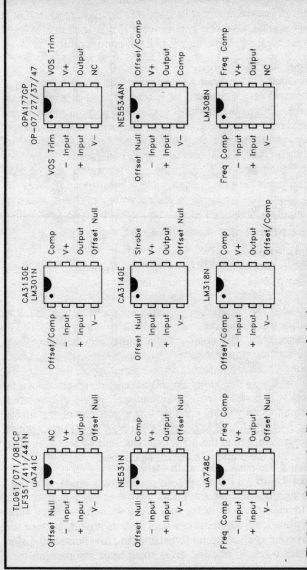

Fig.3.9   Pinout details for a range of single op. amps

93

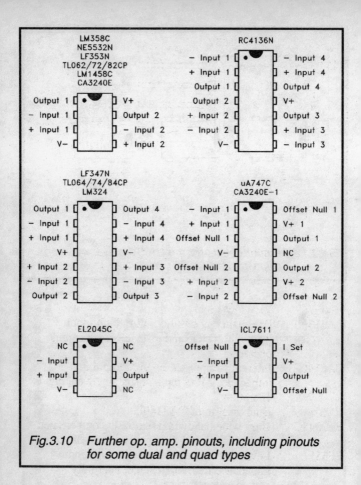

Fig.3.10 Further op. amp. pinouts, including pinouts
for some dual and quad types

as should the basic data in the table which follows this list.
Figures 3.9 to 3.11 show pinout details for a range of operational amplifiers.

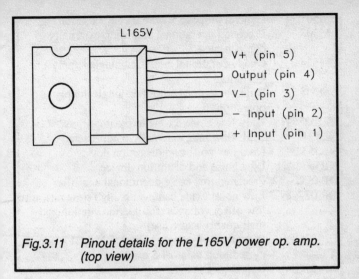

Fig.3.11 Pinout details for the L165V power op. amp. (top view)

7611	Very low supply current
CA3130E	External compensation, ultra high input impedance MOS input stage, single supply operation
CA3140E	Internal compensation, ultra high input impedance MOS input stage, single supply operation
CA3240	Dual version of CA3140E
EL2045C	Ultra wide bandwidth, partially compensated (stable for closed loop gains of two or more)
LF351	Low noise and distortion with high input impedance f.e.t. input stage, internally compensated
LF353	Dual version of LF351
LF347	Quad version of LF351
LF411	Low input offset voltages, low drift, Jfet input stage
LF412	Dual version of LF411
LF441	Low power, Jfet input stage
LF442	Dual version of LF441
LF444	Quad version of LF441

LM301	General purpose, external compensation
LM308	Precision operational amplifier, externally compensated
LM324	Quad operational amplifier, single supply operation
LM358	Dual operational amplifier, single supply operation
LT1028CN8	Ultra low noise for audio preamplifiers
NE531	High slew rate, externally compensated
NE5532N	Dual low noise and distortion device
NE5534AN	Low noise and distortion device
OP-07C	Precision low noise operational amplifier
OP-027GN	Low noise, wide bandwidth, high slew rate, ultra low offset voltages (for instrumentation and high quality audio use)
OP-37GP	Partially compensated OP-27GN (stable for closed loop gains of 5 or more)
OP-77GP	Improved OP-07C
OPA124P	Very high quality precision amplifier
OPA177GP	Precision d.c. amplifier
OPA604AP	Low noise, low distortion, wide bandwidth
RC4136	Quad low noise device
TL061	Low current consumption, Jfet input stage
TL062	Dual version of TL061
TL064	Quad version of TL061
TL071	Low noise, Jfet input stage
TL072	Dual version of TL071
TL074	Quad version of TL071
TL081	General purpose, Jfet input stage
TL082	Dual version of TL081
TL084	Quad version of TL081
TLE2027CP	Ultra low noise and distortion for audio preamps
TLE2037CP	Partially compensated TLE2027CP (stable for closed loop gains of five or more)
µA741C	Industry standard compensated operational amplifier
µA747C	Dual version of µA741C
µA748C	µA741C without internal compensation

Device	B.Width	Supply	S.Rate	Input R	Type/Comp.
CA3130E	15MHz	5-16V 2mA	10V/µs	1.5T	MOS/Ext
CA3140E	4.5MHz	4-36V 4mA	9V/µs	1.5T	MOS/Int
CA3240E	Dual version of CA3140E				
EL2045CN	100MHz	±2-18V 5.2mA	275V/µs	150k	BIP/Int
LF351N	4MHz	±5-18V 1.4mA	13V/µs	1T	BIF/Int
LF353N	Dual version of LF351N				
LF347N	Quad version of LF351N				
LF411N	4MHz	±5-18V 5.6mA	15V/µs	1T	BIF/Int
LF412N	Dual version of LF411N				
LF441N	1MHz	±5-18V 150µA	1V/µs	1T	BIF/Int
LF442N	Dual version of LF441N				
LF444N	Quad version of LF441N				
LM301N	1MHz	±5-18V 1.8mA	0.4V/µs	2M	BIP/Ext
LM308N	1MHz	±5-18V 300µA	0.2V/µs	40M	BIP/Ext
LM324N	1MHz	3-32V 1.5mA	0.5V/µs	1M	BIP/Int
LM1458C	1MHz	±3-18V 3mA	0.5V/µs	1M	BIP/Int
NE531N	1MHz	±5-22V 10mA	35V/µs	20M	BIP/Ext
NE5534AN	10MHz	±3-20V 4mA	13V/µs	100k	BIP/Ext
NE5532N	Dual version of NE5534AN				
OP-07CN	0.5MHz	±2.5-22V 2.7mA	0.17V/µs	33M	BIP/Int
OP-27GP	8MHz	±5-22V 3.5mA	2.8V/µs	4M	BIP/Int
OP37GP	63MHz	±4-20V 3mA	13.5V/µs	4M	BIP/Int
OP-77GP	0.6MHz	±3-20V 1.7mA	0.3V/µs	45M	BIP/Int
OPA177GP	0.6MHz	±3-18V 1.3mA	0.3V/µs	45M	BIP/Int
OPA604AP	20MHz	±4.5-25V 5mA	25V/µs	1T	BIP/Int
RC4136	3MHz	±3-18V 7mA	1Vµs	5M	BIP/Int
TL061CP	1MHz	±2-18V 200uA	3.5V/µs	1T	BIF/Int
TL062CP	Dual version of TL061CP				
TL064	Quad version of TL061CP				
TL071CP	3MHz	±2-18V 1mA	13V/µs	1T	BIF/Int
TL072CP	Dual version of TL071CP				
TL074CP	Quad version of TL071CP				
TL081CP	3MHz	±2-18V 1.4mA	13V/µs	1T	BIF/Int
TL082CP	Dual version of TL081CP				
TL084CP	Quad version of TL081CP				
TLE2027CP	13MHz	±4-22V 3.8mA	2.8V/µs	–	BIP/Int
TLE2037CP	76MHz	±4-22V 3.8mA	7.5V/µs	–	BIP/Int
µA741C	1MHz	±5-18V 1.7mA	0.5V/µs	2M	BIP/Int
µA747C	Dual version of µA741C				
µA748C	1MHz	±5-18V 1.7mA	0.5V/µs	2M	BIP/Ext

Note that where the supply voltage is not given in plus/minus form, the device is suitable for single supply operation, but can still be used with dual balanced supplies. Of course, the dual supply range is half the quoted single supply range (e.g. 3-32V or ± 1.5-16V). With externally compensated devices the bandwidth and slew rate figures depend on the values used in the external compensation circuit. The above figures are no more than a rough guide for externally compensated devices, and in most cases the figures are correct for a device which is compensated for unity voltage gain. The EL2045CN is internally compensated and has no provision for external compensation, but it must be used at closed loop gains of two or more. The OP-37GP is internally compensated for closed loop gains of five or more, and can not be used with external compensation. The same is true of the TLE2037CP. The NE5534AN is internally compensated for closed loop gains of three or more, and it can be used with external compensation for lower gains. In the input resistance column 1T equals one million megohms, and 1.5T equals 1.5 million megohms. In the "Type/Comp." column these abbreviations are used:

BIF   Bifet device (fully integrated Jfet input stage)
BIP   Bipolar device
MOS   MOSFET input stage
Ext   External frequency compensation
Int   Full internal frequency compensation (partial internal compensation where noted).

Pseudo Op Amps
There are a number of operation amplifier style devices available, which are not strictly speaking operational amplifiers. These include voltage comparators, such as the LM311 and LM392. An operational amplifier can be used as a voltage comparator, but a "proper" voltage comparator has potential advantages in some applications, particularly where large differential input voltages are involved. Most devices of this type seem to have open collector output stages, and most are suitable for single supply operation.

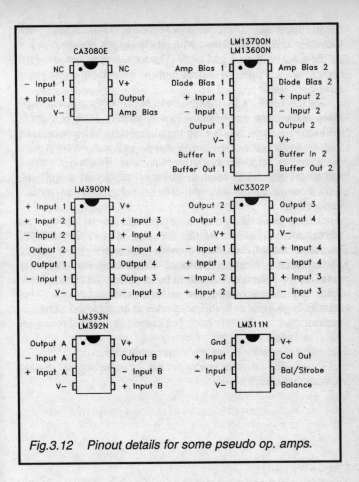

Fig.3.12   Pinout details for some pseudo op. amps.

The LM3900N is a quad "Norton" or current differencing amplifier. The output voltage of a Norton amplifier is governed by the differential input current rather than by the difference in the input voltages, and it must be used in suitably modified circuit configurations. Norton amplifiers are now much less used than they were in the past. One probable reason for this is that they were originally designed to provide operational amplifier style circuits that would operate from a

99

single supply rail. There are now several operational amplifiers that offer high performance with single supply operation, such as the CA3140E and LM358N. These are now the standard choice for applications where Norton amplifiers might once have been used.

The CA3080E, LM13700N, and LM13600N are operational transconductance amplifiers. This is another form of current differencing amplifier, but the most important characteristic of a transconductance amplifier is that its gain can be controlled via a current fed to the amplifier bias input. Transconductance amplifiers are much used in voltage controlled amplifiers, voltage controlled filters, and similar voltage/current control applications.

Current feedback operational amplifiers are a relatively new development. Devices of this type are used in the standard amplifier modes, but they provide superior high frequency performance. Whereas increased closed-loop gain normally gives a proportionate decrease in bandwidth, with current feedback amplifiers the reduction in bandwidth is far less. This enables high gains at high frequencies to be achieved. The d.c. performance is relatively poor, but current feedback devices are only intended for high frequency use, and the lack of d.c. accuracy is usually of no practical importance.

Figure 3.12 provides pinout details for some popular pseudo operational amplifiers.

CHAPTER 4

LOGIC ICs

Although it is not that many years ago that logic integrated circuits in electronic designs for the home constructor were non-existent, they have appeared in an steadily increasing number of projects over the years. We are now at the stage where there seems to be relatively few designs that do not use at least one of these devices, and they quite often appear in circuits that are primarily linear in nature. The number of logic integrated circuits available seems to grow continuously as new devices are produced. These are mainly "improved" versions of existing devices. In fact there are now several families of these "improved" devices.

The original 74** series of TTL chips are still available, but it can be difficult to track down some devices in the range. Most of the standard 74** series are no longer recommended for use in new designs. The original rivals to the 74** TTL family, such as RTL and DTL chips, have been totally obsolete for many years. For new designs it is necessary to resort to one of the new and "improved" ranges of logic devices.

Choosing logic integrated circuits has become a rather confusing subject with so many versions to choose from. Many hobbyists simply stick to the familiar types rather than risking new components which might prove to be costly mistakes. It can also be difficult to determine which alternatives can be substituted for a given device without impairing the performance of a circuit, or even causing it to fail altogether. Here we will take a quick look at the various logic families that are available, and how they differ in terms of performance.

A table of characteristics is provided, and this summarises the information and puts it in an accessible form. However, the information provided is necessarily a generalisation, and it can do nothing more than give a rough guide to the speed, etc., of the various logic families. Individual devices within each family have slightly different propagation delays, maximum operating frequencies, etc., and for detailed information the appropriate manufacturers data sheets must be consulted.

Standard TTL

The standard TTL devices obviously provide a reasonable standard of performance or they would never have been used on such a vast scale. One the other hand, they must have deficiencies or they would not have been ousted by subsequent logic families. They certainly have plenty of good points, but do have some major drawbacks as well. The standard range of TTL integrated circuits are based on ordinary n.p.n. bipolar transistors, and an important consequence of this is that they have quite high levels of current consumption. Devices which contain a few simple gates consume around 20 milliamps, while some of the more complex devices draw supply currents of more than 100 milliamps. This makes standard TTL integrated circuits far from ideal in applications where portability and battery operation is required.

The situation is not helped by the fact that TTL based circuits should ideally be used on a 5 volt supply having a minimum accuracy of plus and minus 5% (i.e. a supply in the range 4.75 volts to 5.25 volts). This is far from convenient if battery operation is required. In practice it is possible to use a 4.5 volt or 6 volt battery as the power source, but results are likely to be less than optimum if anything other than a well regulated 5 volt supply is used.

Another supply related problem is that TTL integrated circuits do not have good immunity to noise on the supply rails. Noise spikes on the supply can easily result in spurious operations of the TTL devices in a circuit. A well regulated 5 volt supply will help to minimise this problem, but it is also necessary to use plenty of supply decoupling capacitors. With large circuits it is normal to use one 100n ceramic decoupling capacitor for every three or four TTL integrated circuits. These capacitors should be distributed as evenly across the circuit board as possible. Some circuit designers seem to take a no compromise approach, and use one decoupling capacitor per TTL device, with each capacitor mounted close to its particular integrated circuit. This probably represents severe overkill, but it is one way of ensuring that supply noise problems are totally avoided.

Although TTL integrated circuits were popular from the outset, they have always had something less than universal acceptance. Their awkward power supply requirements probably represent the main reason that some circuit designers were reluctant to use them. Even where battery operation was not required, a mains power supply providing a well stabilised 5 volts at currents of a few amps was often needed. While such a supply was not technically difficult to produce, it did tend to be quite bulky and expensive.

TTL devices had a big advantage over most other early logic integrated circuits in that they could provide what, at that time anyway, was very high speed operation. In fact the standard TTL devices are respectively fast even by current standards. The maximum usable operating frequency varies significantly from one device to another, and in general the simpler components can operate at higher speeds than the complex ones. Maximum operating frequencies are typically around 30MHz to 40MHz, which is obviously more than adequate for most applications.

Low Power

It is possible for manufacturers to alter the circuit values of TTL devices to produce lower supply currents, and this is basically what was done to produce the low power TTL series of devices. The original TTL integrated circuits have a "74" prefix, followed by a two or three digit serial number (e.g. 74138). The low power versions have the same basic type numbers, but with a "74L" prefix (e.g. "74L138).

Reducing the current consumption results in components that are much better suited to battery operation, but it also produces a reduction in the maximum operating frequency. This reduction in maximum operating frequency is far larger than one might expect. The 74L series have maximum operating frequencies of about 3MHz, which is something under one tenth of the figure for standard TTL components. The current consumption was reduced by a similar amount incidentally. The low power TTL devices never achieved any degree of popularity, and this is probably due to the fact that their characteristics did not compare very favourably with the CMOS logic devices which came along in the early 1970s. They are now obsolete, and are probably unavailable even from suppliers of surplus components.

LS TTL

Of the "improved" TTL families that have stood the test of time, the most important is the LS (low power Schottky) type. These are the new standard range, and are the TTL devices which are most popular for use in new designs. The LS series of components use the same basic type numbers as the standard TTL components, but with a "74LS" prefix (e.g. 74LS138 is the low power Schottky equivalent of the original 74138 device).

74LS versions of TTL integrated circuits are a substantial improvement on the standard devices, as they achieve higher operating speeds but at significantly lower supply currents. The improved speed and reduced current consumption is made possible by the incorporation of Schottky diodes into the circuits. The important difference between a Schottky diode and an ordinary silicon type is that it requires a forward voltage of only about 0.2 volts before it will start to conduct. This compares with a figure of about 0.5 to 0.6 volts for an ordinary silicon diode. They are also capable of high speed operation, which is crucial in the present application.

The speed of ordinary TTL integrated circuits is reduced by the fact that the switching transistors are biased into saturation. This gives problems with charge storage effects, and a slight reluctance for the transistors to switch off again. Higher operating speeds can be obtained if the base currents are regulated so that something just beyond the minimum acceptable drive currents are used. This is achieved using a Schottky diode connected between the collector and base terminals of critical switching transistors, as in Figure 4.1.

If the transistor is switched on to the point where its collector falls to about 0.4 volts, the Schottky diode becomes forward biased and starts to divert the base current through the collector circuit of the transistor. A diode having a fast switching speed is essential, as it must divert the excess base current before the transistor is able to saturate. It is also essential that the diode has a low forward conduction voltage. With an ordinary 0.6 volt switch-on potential the diode would not be biased into conduction until the transistor had been biased into saturation.

The "74LS" circuits are not the just standard TTL types with

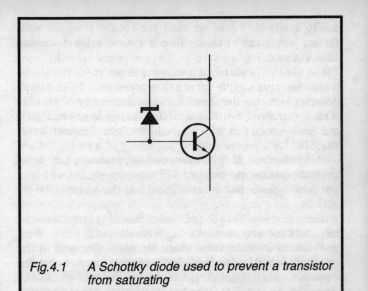

Fig.4.1   A Schottky diode used to prevent a transistor from saturating

a few Schottky diodes added. The circuits have been completely redesigned in order to fully exploit the advantages of Schottky diodes. Switching speeds of 74LS integrated circuits are only slightly better than those of the original TTL devices, being typically about 10 to 20% faster. This level of performance is achieved at only about a fifth of the standard TTL supply current though. The 74LS range therefore provides a substantial step forward in performance, and at a cost which is currently about 30% less than that of the standard TTL components. It is for this reason that the 74LS range has largely usurped the ordinary TTL devices.

The Rest
There are other families of TTL integrated circuits which exploit Schottky diodes in order to obtain improved performance. The "74S" range have slightly higher current consumptions than their ordinary "74" series equivalents, but are some three to four times faster. Many devices in the 74S series can operate with input frequencies of well óver 100MHz. For some time these were the fastest TTL components that were

readily available, but as we shall see shortly, there are now devices which offer similar speeds but with lower current consumptions.

The "74ALS" (advanced low power Schottky) devices were at one time tipped to take over as the new standard TTL range. However, in reality they never achieved dominance of the TTL market, with the "LS" range providing the combination of price and performance that better suited most users' requirements. The "74ALS" devices are now something of a rarity, and are virtually obsolete. They achieve operating speeds that are nearly double those of the standard TTL components, but with current consumptions that are only about half those of the "74LS" devices.

There is also a "74AS" (advanced Schottky) range incidentally, but these never achieved a substantial market share. They have current consumptions which are much the same as the standard Schottky devices, but the maximum operating frequencies are in the region of 200MHz. This probably makes them the fastest TTL devices that have been produced commercially.

CMOS

CMOS is an acronym, and it stands for "complementary metal oxide silicon" (although some prefer "complementary metal oxide semiconductor"). Integrated circuits which are formed using this technology are based on enhancement mode MOSFETs ("metal oxide silicon field effect transistors"), and not ordinary bipolar transistors. As the "complementary" part of the name indicates, both N channel and P channel MOSFETs are used in these devices.

Looking at things from the users standpoint, the main difference between an enhancement MOSFET and a bipolar transistor is that the latter is current operated whereas MOSFETs are voltage operated. A bipolar transistor remains switched off until the input voltage to the base terminal reaches about 0.6 volts. Up to this point very little current flows. Raising the input voltage above 0.6 volts results in a sudden increase in the base current, and the device begins to switch on. With an input potential of only about 0.7 volts the input current becomes quite large, and the device is switched on to saturation point.

Taking the input voltage much higher is likely to cause an excessive base current, and the destruction of the transistor.

The forward transfer characteristic of an enhancement mode MOSFET is very different. These devices are switched off until the input voltage to the gate terminal reaches about 0.8 volts or so. Increasing the gate voltage above this level results in the device gradually switching on, with saturation point being reached at a gate potential of a few volts. The input resistance of a field effect transistor is extremely high, and in the case of a MOSFET it is often more than a million megohms (1,000,000,000,000 ohms). This means that the current flow into the gate of a MOSFET is negligible, and is actually far too low to measure using ordinary test equipment.

CMOS logic integrated circuits therefore have extremely high input resistances, and on the face of it they should have what is effectively infinite fanout capability. If high speed operation is not required, they do indeed have what for most practical purposes can be regarded as infinite fanout. If high speed operation is needed, the input capacitance must be taken into account. This gives increased loading at high frequencies which reduces the fanout figure to about 50. However, this is still so high that it is unlikely to be a limiting factor when designing practical CMOS logic circuits.

Micro Power
The very high input resistance of CMOS logic devices is a very useful characteristic, but their main advantage over most other types of logic integrated circuit is their low current consumption at low operating speeds. The output stages of CMOS integrated circuits consist of complementary (PMOS/NMOS) transistors which act as electronic switches. They are connected in the manner shown in Figure 4.2. When one of the transistors is switched on it has a resistance that is typically around 300 ohms. When one of the transistors is switched off it has a resistance that is extremely high (normally at least a thousand megohms). When an output is high it has a circuit equivalent to that of Figure 4.3(a), and while it is low is has a circuit equivalent to that of Figure 4.3(b).

The important point to note here is that in both cases the total resistance across the supply lines is extremely high, and

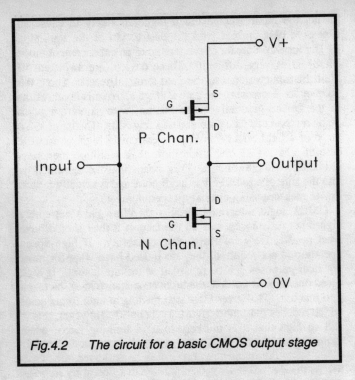

Fig.4.2   The circuit for a basic CMOS output stage

there is an insignificant current flow. On the face of it, CMOS logic integrated circuits have a negligible current consumption. Unfortunately, in reality matters are not quite as rosy as this. The first point to note is that any current which flows into a load connected at an output (a l.e.d. indicator for example) will be added to the normal current consumption of the device driving the load. The second point is that a pulse of current is consumed each time an output changes state. In effect, one switch is turned on to a significant degree before the other one switches off properly.

If a CMOS device is not driving a current through a load of some kind, and it is either static or operating at a very low frequency, it will draw an insignificant supply current. If it changes state at a high frequency there will be a large number of current pulses drawn from the supply in a given period of

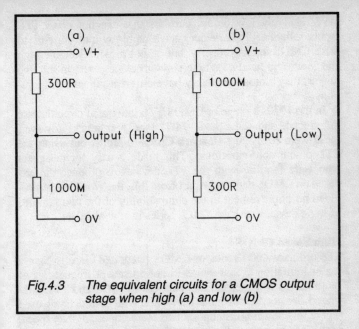

*Fig.4.3   The equivalent circuits for a CMOS output
          stage when high (a) and low (b)*

time, and a relatively high supply current. In general, the higher the operating frequency of a CMOS logic device, the higher
the supply current it will consume. At low operating frequencies CMOS devices provide a massive power saving in comparison to standard TTL logic devices. At high frequencies it is
possible for a CMOS device to have a higher current consumption than a TTL equivalent.

CMOS logic integrated circuits are therefore well suited to
applications that require low levels of current consumption, and
which involve relatively low operating frequencies. In reality
they give significant power savings in practically any application, since few circuits have every stage operating at high
speed. In "real world" circuits it is normally the case that some
stages operate at high speed, while most of the others operate
at low frequencies or are static for much of the time.

The original CMOS logic family (the "4000" series) was
launched as a rival to the TTL range. The two ranges of devices
were, and remain, almost totally incompatible. CMOS devices

have relatively low output currents that can not drive TTL inputs reliably. TTL devices have ample output currents to drive CMOS inputs properly, but do not provide suitable high and low logic levels. Where similar devices exist in the two ranges, they almost invariably have different pinout configurations.

In the 1970s a range of CMOS TTL integrated circuits were introduced, and these had "74C" type numbers. However, these were really just standard CMOS circuits, but using the TTL pinout configurations. This made it easy for designers who were familiar with the TTL devices to produce circuits based on CMOS devices. Apart from this, the "74C" range provided no improvement in the compatibility of the two families of logic devices, and the "74C" series is now obsolete.

High Speed CMOS

The ordinary 4000 series of CMOS integrated circuits have a major limitation in that they will not operate at frequencies of more than a few megahertz. This gave CMOS and TTL integrated circuits their own market niches, with CMOS being used where low power consumption was more important than speed, and TTL being used where high speed was of paramount importance. These days there is an option which gives the best of both worlds. This is to use devices from one of the high speed CMOS logic families.

There are two common types, which are the "74HC" and "74HCT" series. These are both based on the same technology, and this technology is a refinement of the original CMOS type, rather than something completely new. It provides operation at far higher frequencies than the "4000" series can manage, and it also produces a much higher output current capability. The difference between the "74HC" and "74HCT" series is that the former operates at normal CMOS switching levels, whereas the latter operates at TTL logic levels.

The "4000" CMOS devices can operate over a supply voltage range of 3 to 15 volts, and the maximum logic 0 voltage is 30% of the supply voltage. The minimum logic 1 potential is 70% of the supply voltage. The "74HC" devices can only operate over a supply voltage range of 2 to 6 volts, and they are primarily intended for use in circuits that include components from the standard "4000" range. Of course, circuits can also be based solely on "74HC" series devices.

For TTL logic circuits the supply potential should normally be 5 volts, and the maximum acceptable logic 0 level is 0.8 volts. The minimum legitimate logic 1 level is 2 volts. The "74HCT" range are primarily intended for use in circuits that include devices from other TTL families. CMOS integrated circuits, unlike TTL devices, have good immunity to noise on the supply rails. The "74HC" range retain this excellent noise immunity, but the "74HCT" range does not. Therefore, if a circuit is to be based solely on high speed CMOS integrated circuits, the "74HC" series would seem to be a better choice than the "74HCT" range.

For both ranges of high speed CMOS devices the current consumption varies from a negligible level when static or operating at low frequencies, to a level that is comparable to equivalent "74LS" devices when operating at very high frequencies. The maximum operating frequency for high speed CMOS devices is much the same as for equivalent "74LS" components. There are advanced high speed CMOS devices which can operate at frequencies of over 100MHz (the "74AC" series), but as yet these are quite expensive, and difficult to obtain.

Which TTL?

With several types of TTL integrated circuit readily available, selecting the best type for a given application can be difficult. If you are following a published design, then it would clearly be advisable to use the exact types specified in the components list. If you are designing your own circuits, then "74LS" components would seem to be the obvious choice. It is probably only worth using a different type if the "74LS" devices are deficient in some way. If their current consumption is too high, then devices in the "74HCT" or "74HC" series would be a better choice, particularly if much of the circuit is operating at low frequencies, or in an intermittent fashion. Being realistic about matters, if low current consumption is important, and high operating speed is of no consequence, then "4000" series CMOS integrated circuits may well be a better choice than any TTL range. Where very high operating speeds are needed,

"74ALS" or "74AC" devices should be suitable, if you can obtain them.

It has to be pointed out that the "74HC" and "74HCT" devices are starting to become cheaper than the "74LS" equivalents. We would seem to be reaching the point where using high speed CMOS components has become cheaper than using "74LS" types. If high speed CMOS components can be obtained more cheaply than the "74LS" types, then a circuit based solely on "74HC" devices is certainly the best choice. Possibly the "74LS" series will become largely obsolete over the next few years.

In general there is no difficulty in using a mixture of TTL types. The obvious exception is the "74HC" series, with its CMOS "4000" series logic levels. If high speed CMOS devices are used with other types of TTL integrated circuit, it is the "74HCT" range which must be utilized. The main reason for using a mixture of TTL types is as an economy measure in a circuit where only certain stages need to operate at high frequencies. Devices from a high speed TTL range (e.g. "74ALS" types) would be used in the critical stages, with ordinary "74LS" or "74HCT" components being used elsewhere. Another reason for using a mixture of TTL types is that it is not always possible to find the devices you require in the appropriate TTL family. For example, the popular 74121 monostable only seems to be available as a standard TTL device, and is not available as a 74LS121, 74HCT121, etc.

The main point to watch when mixing TTL types is the fanout of the various devices in the circuit. With certain TTL combinations the fanout is very low indeed. In particular, 74HCT outputs can only drive two standard TTL inputs. This table shows the fanout for three common TTL families when used in any combination.

TTL Type (Driving)	Maximum No. of Inputs Driven		
	74	74LS	74HCT
74	10	40	100+
74 buffers	30	60	100+
74LS	5	20	100+
74LS buffers	15	60	100+
74HCT	2	10	100+
74HCT buffers	4	15	100+

This table summarises the basic characteristics of several families of logic devices.

	Std TTL	LS TTL	ALS TTL	STTL
Supply Voltage	5V (+5%)	5V (+5%)	5V (+5%)	5V (+5%)
DC Fanout	40	20	20	50
Maximum Low Input V	0.8V	0.8V	0.8V	0.8V
Minimum High Input V	2V	2V	2V	2V
Maximum Low Output V	0.4V	0.5V	0.5V	0.5V
Minimum High Output V	2.4V	2.7V	2.7V	2.7V
DC Noise Margin (L/H)	0.3/0.7	0.3/0.7	0.4/0.7	0.3/0.7
Input Cur. (L/H µA)	40/1600	20/400	20/200	–
Output Cur. L/H mA)	16/0.4	8/0.4	8/0.4	20/–
Temp. Range (Degrees C)	0/70	0/70	0/70	0/70
Typical Max Frequency	35MHz	40MHz	70MHz	120MHz
Relative Power Diss.	1	0.2	0.1	1

	Std CMOS	74HC	74HCT	FACT
Supply Voltage	3-18V	2-6V	5V (±10%)	2-6V
DC Fanout	1	10	10	60
Maximum Low Input V	1.5V	0.9V	0.8V	1.35V

Minimum High Input V	3.5V	3.15V	2V	3.15V
Maximum Low Output V	0.05V	0.1V	0.1V	0.1V
Minimum High Output V	4.95V	4.9V	4.9V	4.9V
DC Noise Margin (L/H)	1.45/1.45	0.8/1.25	–/–	1.25/1.25
Input Cur. (L/H µA)	0.3/0.3	1/1	1/1	1/1
Output Cur. L/H mA)	2.1/0.45	4/4	4/4	24/24
Temp. Range (Degrees C)	–40/+85	–40/+85	–40/+85	–40/+85
Typical Max Frequency	35MHz	40MHz	70MHz	120MHz
Relative Power Diss.	1	0.2	0.1	1

The following list covers TTL devices, and gives both the function and package type for each device that is listed. This should be useful when trying to find the function of a particular device. The smaller lists after the main one are useful when looking for a device that has the required function. Not all TTL devices are included, but most of those that are readily available to non-professional users are listed here.

Device	Function	Package
7400	Quad 2 input NAND gate	14 pin DIL
7401	Quad 2 input NAND gate (open collector)	14 pin DIL
7402	Quad 2 input NOR gate	14 pin DIL
7403	Quad 2 input NAND gate (open collector)	14 pin DIL
7404	Hex inverter	14 pin DIL
7405	Hex inverter (open collector)	14 pin DIL

7406	Hex inverter/buffer (open collector)	14 pin DIL
7407	Hex buffer	14 pin DIL
7408	Quad 2 input AND gate	14 pin DIL
7409	Quad 2 input AND gate (open collector)	14 pin DIL
7410	Triple 3 input NAND gate	14 pin DIL
7411	Triple 3 input AND gate	14 pin DIL
7412	Triple 3 input NAND gate (open collector)	14 pin DIL
7413	Dual 4 input NAND (trigger)	14 pin DIL
7414	Hex Schmitt trigger	14 pin DIL
7415	Triple 3 input AND gate (open collector)	14 pin DIL
7416	Hex inverter/buffer (open collector)	14 pin DIL
7417	Hex buffer (open collector)	14 pin DIL
7420	Dual 4 input NAND gate	14 pin DIL
7421	Dual 4 input AND gate	14 pin DIL
7422	Dual 4 input NAND gate (open collector)	14 pin DIL
7425	Dual 4 input NOR gate (with strobe)	14 pin DIL
7426	Quad 2 input NAND gate (open collector)	14 pin DIL
7427	Triple 3 input NOR gate	14 pin DIL
7428	Quad 2 input NOR buffer	14 pin DIL
7430	8 input NAND gate	14 pin DIL
7432	Quad 2 input OR gate	14 pin DIL
7433	Quad 2 input NOR buffer (open collector)	14 pin DIL
7437	Quad 2 input NAND buffer (open collector)	14 pin DIL
7438	Quad 2 input AND buffer (open collector)	14 pin DIL
7440	Dual 4 input NAND buffer	14 pin DIL
7442	BCD to decimal decoder (1 of 10)	16 pin DIL
7447	BCD to 7 seg decoder/driver	16 pin DIL
7448	BCD to 7 seg decoder/driver	16 pin DIL
7451	Complex AND/OR/inverter gate	14 pin DIL

7454	Complex AND/OR/inverter gate	14 pin DIL
7470	JK edge triggered flip/flop	14 pin DIL
7472	JK pulse triggered flip/flop	14 pin DIL
7473	Dual JK flip/flop	14 pin DIL
7474	Dual D type flip/flop	14 pin DIL
7475	Dual 2 bit transparent latch	16 pin DIL
7476	Dual JK flip/flop	16 pin DIL
7481	16 bit RAM	14 pin DIL
7483	4 bit full adder	16 pin DIL
7485	4 bit magnitude comparator	16 pin DIL
7486	Quad 2 input XOR gate	14 pin DIL
7489	64 bit RAM	16 pin DIL
7490	Decade counter	14 pin DIL
7492	Divide by 12 counter	14 pin DIL
7493	4 bit binary ripple counter	14 pin DIL
7495	4 bit shift register	14 pin DIL
7496	bit shift register	16 pin DIL
74107	Dual JK flip/flop	14 pin DIL
74109	Dual JK flip/flop	16 pin DIL
74112	Dual JK flip/flop	16 pin DIL
74113	Dual JK flip/flop	14 pin DIL
74118	Hex S/R latch	16 pin DIL
74121	Monostable	14 pin DIL
74122	Retriggerable monostable	14 pin DIL
74123	Dual retriggerable monostable	16 pin DIL
74125	Quad 3 state buffer	14 pin DIL
74126	Quad 3 state buffer	14 pin DIL
74132	Quad 2 input NAND trigger	14 pin DIL
74136	Quad 2 input XOR gate (open collector)	14 pin DIL
74137	3 to 8 line decoder	16 pin DIL
74138	3 to 8 line decoder	16 pin DIL
74139	Dual 1 of 4 decoder/demultiplexer	16 pin DIL
74141	BCD to decimal decoder/driver	16 pin DIL
74145	BCD to decimal decoder (open collector)	16 pin DIL
74150	16 input multiplexer	24 pin DIL
74151	8 input multiplexer	16 pin DIL
74153	Dual 4 to 1 multiplexer	16 pin DIL
74154	1 of 16 decoder/demultiplexer	24 pin DIL

74155	Dual 2 to 4 line decoder	16 pin DIL
74156	Dual 2 to 4 line decoder (open collector)	16 pin DIL
74157	Quad 2 input data selector (inv)	16 pin DIL
74158	Quad 2 input date selector (inv.)	16 pin DIL
74160	4 bit decade counter	16 pin DIL
74161	4 bit binary counter	16 pin DIL
74162	4 bit decade counter (sync)	16 pin DIL
74163	4 bit binary counter (sync)	16 pin DIL
74164	8 bit ser in par out shift reg	14 pin DIL
74165	8 bit par in ser out shift reg	16 pin DIL
74166	8 bit ser/par in ser out shift reg	16 pin DIL
74168	4 bit up/down sync decade counter	16 pin DIL
74169	4 bit up/down sync binary counter	16 pin DIL
74170	4 × 4 register file	16 pin DIL
74173	Quad D type flip/flop (3 state)	16 pin DIL
74174	Hex D type flip/flop	16 pin DIL
74175	Quad D type flip/flop	16 pin DIL
74181	4 bit ALU	24 pin DIL
74190	Presettable BCD up/down counter	16 pin DIL
74191	Presettable 4 bit binary up/down counter	16 pin DIL
74192	Presettable BCD decade up/down counter	16 pin DIL
74193	Presettable 4 bit binary up/down counter	16 pin DIL
74194	4 bit bidirectional universal shift register	16 pin DIL
74195	4 bit parallel access shift reg	16 pin DIL
74196	Presettable decade ripple counter	14 pin DIL
74197	Presettable 4 bit binary counter	14 pin DIL
74221	Dual monostable	16 pin DIL
74237	3 to 8 line decoder	16 pin DIL
74238	3 to 8 line decoder	16 pin DIL
74240	Octal 3 state inverter/buffer	20 pin DIL
74241	Octal 3 state buffer	20 pin DIL
74242	Quad inverting transceiver (3 state)	14 pin DIL
74243	Quad transceiver (3 state)	14 pin DIL
74244	Octal 3 state buffer	20 pin DIL

74245	Octal 3 state transceiver	20 pin DIL
74251	8 input multiplexer (3 state)	16 pin DIL
74253	Dual 4 input multiplexer (3 state)	16 pin Dil
74257	Quad 2 to 1 line data selector (3 state outputs, non-inverting)	16 pin DIL
74258	Quad 2 to 1 line data selector (3 state outputs, inverting)	16 pin DIL
74259	8 bit addressable latch	16 pin DIL
74260	Dual 5 input NOR gate	16 pin DIL
74261	Multiplex decoder	14 pin DIL
74266	Quad 2 input XNOR gate (open collector)	14 pin DIL
74273	Octal D type flip/flop	20 pin DIL
74279	Quad S/R latch	16 pin DIL
74283	4 bit full adder with fast carry	16 pin DIL
74290	Decade counter	14 pin DIL
74292	Programmable divider/timer	16 pin DIL
74293	4 bit binary ripple counter	14 pin DIL
74297	Digital phase locked loop filter	16 pin DIL
74298	Quad 2 port register, true and complementary outputs	16 pin DIL
74323	8 bit universal shift/storage reg	20 pin DIL
74365	Hex buffer, 3 state, gated enable inputs	16 pin DIL
74366	Hex inverter, 3 state, gated enable inputs	16 pin DIL
74367	Hex buffer, 3 state, enable inputs	16 pin DIL
74368	Hex inverter, 3 state, enable inputs	16 pin DIL
74373	Octal transparent latch, 3 state	20 pin DIL
74374	Octal D type flip/flop, 3 state	20 pin DIL
74377	Octal D type flip/flop with clock enable	20 pin DIL
74378	Hex D type flip/flop with clock enable	16 pin DIL
74379	Quad D type flip/flop with clock enable	16 pin DIL
74390	Dual decade ripple counter	16 pin DIL
74393	Dual 4 bit binary ripple counter	14 pin DIL
74395	4 bit cascadeable shift register,	

	3 state outputs	16 pin DIL
74399	Quad 2 port register, single rail output	16 pin DIL
74490	Decade counter	16 pin DIL
74534	Octal D type flip/flop	20 pin DIL
74601	64K Dynamic RAM refresh controller	20 pin DIL
74604	Octal 2 input multiplexed latch, 3 state outputs	28 pin DIL
74629	Voltage controlled oscillator	16 pin DIL
74670	4×4 register file, 3 state	16 pin DIL
74684	8 bit magnitude comparator	20 pin DIL
74688	8 bit magnitude comparator	20 pin DIL

AND Gates

7408	quad 2 input
7409	quad 2 input (open collector)
7411	triple 3 input
7415	triple 3 input (open collector)
7421	dual 4 input

NAND Gates

7400	quad 2 input
7401	quad 2 input (open collector)
7403	quad 2 input (open collector)
7410	triple 3 input
7420	dual 4 input
7422	dual 4 input (open collector)
7426	quad 2 input (open collector)
7430	single 8 input
7437	quad 2 input buffer
7438	quad 2 input buffer (open collector)
74132	quad 2 input (Schmitt trigger)

OR Gates

7432	quad 2 input

NOR Gates

7402	quad 2 input
7425	dual 4 input

119

7427	triple 3 input
7428	quad 2 input buffer
7433	quad 2 input (open collector)
74260	dual 5 input

Other Gates/inverters/Buffers

7404	hex inverter
7405	hex inverter (open collector)
7406	hex inverter (open collector)
7407	hex buffer (open collector)
7414	hex inverting trigger
7416	hex inverter (open collector)
7417	hex buffer (open collector, 30V)
7486	quad 2 input XOR
74266	quad 2 input XNOR (open collector)
74125	quad tristate buffer (active low)
74126	quad tristate buffer (active high)
74244	octal tristate buffer
74245	octal transceiver
74365	hex 3 state
74366	hex inverting 3 state
74367	hex 3 state
74368	hex inverting 3 state

Flip/Flops

7470	positive edge triggered JK
7472	JK master slave
7473	dual JK with clear
7474	dual D type (edge triggered)
7475	4 bit bistable latch
7476	dual JK with clear and preset
74107	dual JK with clear
74109	dual positive edge triggered JK
74112	dual negative edge triggered JK
74174	hex D type
74175	quad D type
74273	octal D type
74373	octal transparent latch
74374	octal D type (3 state)

| 74377 | octal D type (common enable) |
| 74534 | inverting octal D type (3 state) |

Shift Registers

7495	4 bit
7496	5 bit
74164	8 bit
74165	8 bit
74166	8 bit
74170	4 × 4 register file
74194	4 bit
74195	4 bit parallel
74395	4 bit cascadeable

Counters

7490	decade
7492	divide by 12
7493	4 bit binary
74160	4 bit decade
74161	4 bit binary
74162	4 bit decade (synchronous)
74163	4 bit binary (synchronous)
74169	4 bit binary
74190	BCD counter
74191	binary counter
74192	BCD dual clock
74193	binary dual clock
74196	presettable decade
74197	presettable binary
74390	dual decade
74490	decade

Decoder/Drivers

7442	BCD to decimal decoder
7447	BCD to 7 segment decoder
7448	BCD to 7 segment decoder
74137	3 to 8 line
74138	3 to 8 line
74139	dual 2 to 4 line decoder
74141	BCD to decimal decoder

74145	BCD to decimal decoder
74150	1 of 16 data selector
74151	1 of 8 data selector
74153	dual 4 to 1 line data selector
74154	4 to 16 line decoder
74155	dual 2 to 4 line
74156	dual 2 to 4 line (open collector)
74157	quad 2 to 1 line data selector
74158	quad 2 to 1 line data selector
74237	3 to 8 line decoder
74238	3 to 8 line decoder
74251	data selector
74257	quad data selector

Miscellaneous

7485	4 bit magnitude comparator
74121	monostable
74122	retriggerable monostable
74123	dual retriggerable monostable
74629	dual voltage controlled oscillator
74684	8 bit magnitude comparator
74688	8 bit magnitude comparator

Figure 4.4 to 4.11 provide pinout details for a wide range of TTL chips.

CMOS

These lists are the CMOS equivalents to the TTL ones provided previously. Again, the entire range of devices is not covered, but most of those that are available to the electronics hobbyist are included here.

Device	Function	Package
4000	dual 3 input NOR gate and inverter	14 pin DIL
4001	quad 2 input NOR gate	14 pin DIL
4002	dual 4 input NOR gate	14 pin DIL
4006	18 stage static shift register	14 pin DIL
4007	dual complementary pair plus inverter	14 pin DIL
4008	4 bit full adder	14 pin DIL

122

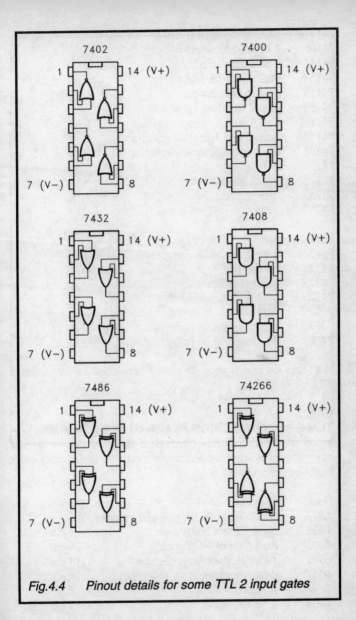

Fig.4.4   Pinout details for some TTL 2 input gates

123

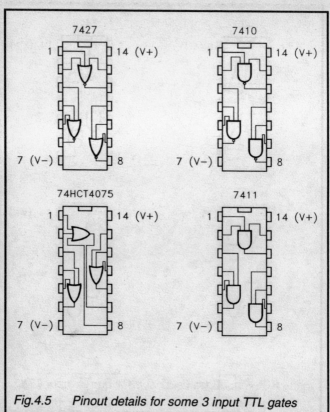

Fig.4.5   Pinout details for some 3 input TTL gates

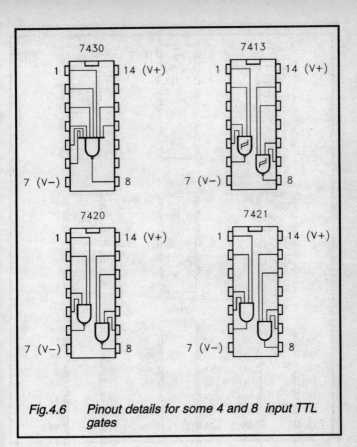

Fig.4.6   Pinout details for some 4 and 8 input TTL
           gates

125

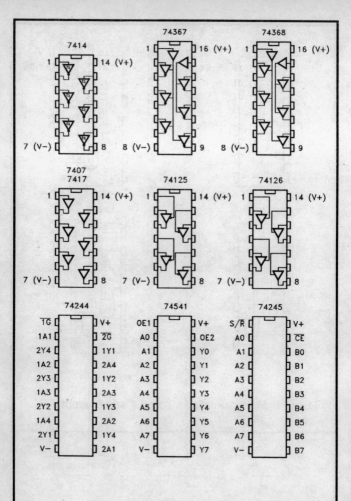

Fig.4.7   Pinout details for some TTL buffers/inverters

126

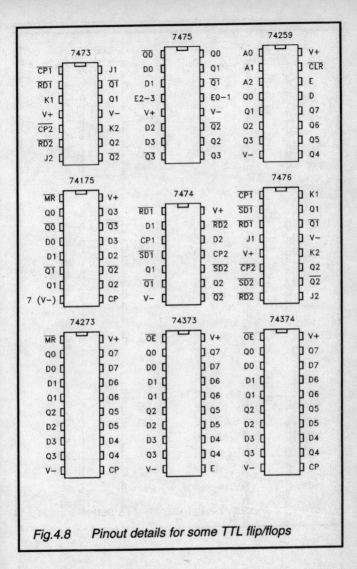

Fig.4.8   Pinout details for some TTL flip/flops

127

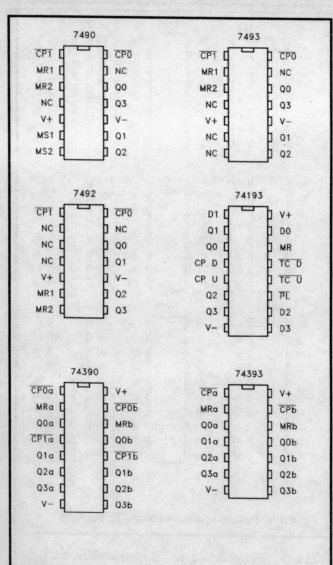

Fig.4.9   Pinout details for some TTL counters

128

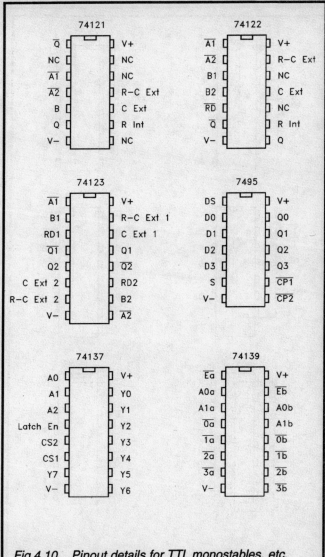

Fig.4.10   Pinout details for TTL monostables, etc.

129

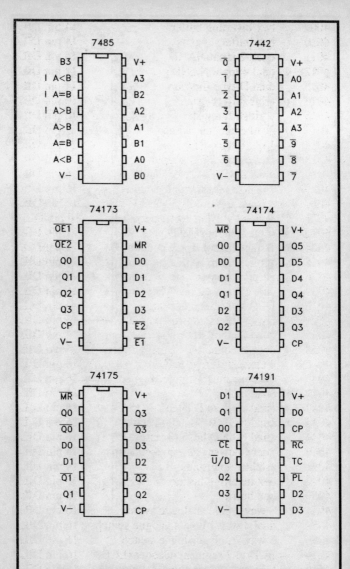

Fig.4.11   Pinout details for miscellaneous TTL chips

130

4009	hex inverting buffer	14 pin DIL
4010	hex buffer	14 pin DIL
4011	quad 2 input NAND	14 pin DIL
4012	dual 4 input NAND	14 pin DIL
4013	dual D type flip/flop	14 pin DIL
4014	8 bit shift register	16 pin DIL
4015	8 bit shift register	16 pin DIL
4016	quad analogue switch	14 pin DIL
4017	1 of 10 decoder	16 pin DIL
4018	presettable BCD counter	16 pin DIL
4019	quad AND/OR select gate	16 pin DIL
4020	14 stage binary ripple counter	16 pin DIL
4021	8 stage static shift register	16 pin DIL
4022	divide by 8 and 1 of 8 decoder	16 pin DIL
4023	triple 3 input NAND gate	14 pin DIL
4024	7 stage binary ripple counter	14 pin DIL
4025	triple 3 input NOR gate	14 pin DIL
4026	decade counter/7 segment driver	16 pin DIL
4027	dual JK master slave flip/flop	16 pin DIL
4028	BCD to decimal decoder	16 pin DIL
4029	presettable up/down counter	16 pin DIL
4030	quad 2 input XOR gate	14 pin DIL
4033	decade counter/7 segment driver	16 pin DIL
4035	4 stage shift register	16 pin DIL
4040	12 stage binary ripple counter	16 pin DIL
4041	quad buffer	14 pin DIL
4042	quad clocked D latch	16 pin DIL
4043	quad NOR R/S latch (3 state)	16 pin DIL
4044	quad NAND latch (3 state)	16 pin DIL
4046	micro-power phase locked loop	16 pin DIL
4047	astable/monostable	14 pin DIL
4049	hex inverting buffer	16 pin DIL
4050	hex buffer	16 pin DIL
4051	8 way 1 pole analogue switch	16 pin DIL
4052	dual 4 way 1 pole analogue switch	16 pin DIL
4053	3 way 2 pole analogue switch	16 pin DIL
4056	BCD to 7 segment decoder (LCD)	16 pin DIL
4060	Osc and 14 stage binary counter	16 pin DIL
4063	4 bit magnitude comparator	16 pin DIL
4066	quad analogue switch	14 pin DIL

4067	16 way 1 pole analogue switch	24 pin DIL
4068	8 input AND/NAND gate	14 pin DIL
4069	hex inverter	14 pin DIL
4070	quad 2 input XOR gate	14 pin DIL
4071	quad 2 input OR gate	14 pin DIL
4072	dual 4 input OR gate	14 pin DIL
4073	triple 3 input AND gate	14 pin DIL
4075	triple 3 input OR gate	14 pin DIL
4076	4 bit D type register	16 pin DIL
4077	quad 2 input XNOR gate	14 pin DIL
4078	8 input NOR gate	14 pin DIL
4081	quad 2 input AND gate	14 pin DIL
4082	dual 4 input AND gate	14 pin DIL
4093	quad 2 input NAND Schmitt trigger	14 pin DIL
4094	8 stage shift register	16 pin DIL
4098	dual monostable	16 pin DIL
4099	8 bit addressable latch	16 pin DIL
40103	8 stage counter	16 pin DIL
40105	FIFO register	16 pin DIL
40106	hex Schmitt trigger	14 pin DIL
40107	dual 2 input NAND buffer	8 pin DIL
40108	4 × 4 multiport register	24 pin DIL
40109	quad voltage shifter	16 pin DIL
40110	decade up/down counter/7 segment decoder/driver	16 pin DIL
40174	hex D type flip/flop	16 pin DIL
40181	4 bit logic unit	24 pin DIL
40182	look ahead carry generator	16 pin DIL
40257	quad 2 to 1 line data selector	16 pin DIL
4416	quad analogue switch	14 pin DIL
4419	keyboard to binary encoder	16 pin DIL
4502	strobed hex inverter	16 pin DIL
4503	hex buffer (3 state)	16 pin DIL
4508	dual 4 bit latch	24 pin DIL
4510	BCD presettable counter	16 pin DIL
4511	BCD 7 segment decoder/driver	16 pin DIL
4512	8 channel data selector	16 pin DIL
4514	4 to 16 line decoder	24 pin DIL
4515	4 to 16 line decoder	24 pin DIL
4516	presettable binary counter	16 pin DIL

4518	dual BCD counter	16 pin DIL
4520	dual binary counter	16 pin DIL
4526	4 bit binary counter	16 pin DIL
4528	dual monostable	16 pin DIL
4532	8 bit priority encoder	16 pin DIL
4536	programmable counter	16 pin DIL
4541	programmable timer	14 pin DIL
4555	dual binary 1 of 4 decoder	16 pin DIL
45100	4×4 crosspoint switch	16 pin DIL

AND Gates

4081	quad 2 input
4073	triple 3 input
4082	dual 4 input

NAND Gates

4011	quad 2 input
4023	triple 3 input
4012	dual 4 input
4068	single 8 input
4093	quad 2 input (Schmitt trigger)

OR Gates

4071	quad 2 input
4075	triple 3 input
4072	dual 4 input

NOR Gates

4001	quad 2 input
4025	triple 3 input
4002	dual 4 input
4078	single 8 input
4000	dual 3 input plus inverter

Other Gates/Buffers/Inverters

4007	Complementary pair plus inverter
4009	hex inverter
4010	hex buffer
4041	quad (true/complement)
4049	hex inverter (high current)

133

4050	hex buffer (high current)
4069	hex inverter
4070	quad 2 input XOR
4077	quad 2 input XNOR
40106	hex inverting trigger
4502	hex inverting (3 state)
4503	hex tristate buffer

Flip/Flops

4013	dual D type
4027	dual JK master slave
4042	quad clocked D latch
4043	quad 3 state NOR R/S latch
4044	quad 3 state NAND R/S latch
4076	4 bit D type register
40108	4 × 4 multiport register
40174	hex D type
4508	dual 4 bit latch

Shift Registers

4006	18 bit shift register
4014	8 bit shift register
4015	8 bit shift register
4021	8 stage static shift register
4035	4 stage static shift register
4094	8 stage shift register
40105	FIFO register

Counters

4017	divide by ten and 1 of 10 decoder
4018	presettable BCD counter
4020	14 stage binary ripple counter
4022	divide by 8 and 1 of 8 decoder
4024	7 stage binary ripple counter
4026	decade counter and 7 segment decoder/driver
4029	presettable up/down counter
4033	decade counter and 7 segment decoder/driver
4040	12 stage binary ripple counter
4060	14 stage binary counter and oscillator
40103	8 stage counter

40110	decade up/down counter and 7 segment decoder/driver
4510	presettable counter
4516	binary presettable counter
4518	dual BCD counter
4520	dual binary counter
4526	4 bit binary counter
4536	programmable counter

Decoders, Etc.

4017	1 of 10
4022	1 of 8
4026	decade counter and 7 segment decoder
4028	BCD to decimal decoder
4033	decade counter and 7 segment decoder
4051	8 channel analogue multiplexer
4052	dual 4 channel analogue multiplexer
4053	triple 2 channel multiplexer
4056	BCD to 7 segment decoder (LCD)
4067	16 channel analogue multiplexer
4419	keyboard to binary encoder
4511	BCD to 7 segment decoder
4514	4 to 16 line decoder
4515	4 to 16 line decoder
4532	8 bit priority encoder

Miscellaneous

4016	quad spst analogue switch
4046	micro-power phase locked loop
4047	astable/monostable
4063	magnitude comparator
4066	quad spst analogue switch
4098	dual monostable
40181	4 bit logic unit
4416	quad spst analogue switch
4541	programmable timer
45100	4 × 4 crosspoint switch

Figures 4.12 to 4.18 provide pinout details for a wide range of CMOS logic devices.

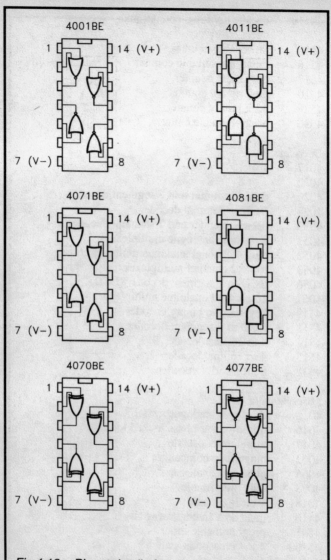

Fig.4.12   Pinout details for some 2 input CMOS gates

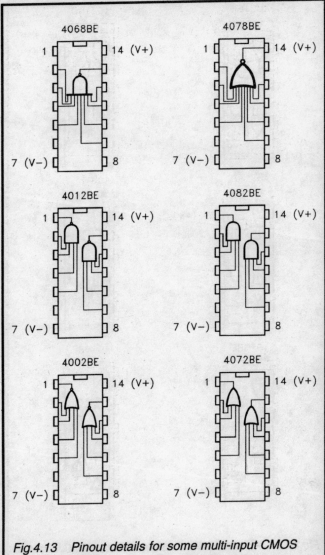

Fig.4.13   Pinout details for some multi-input CMOS
gates

137

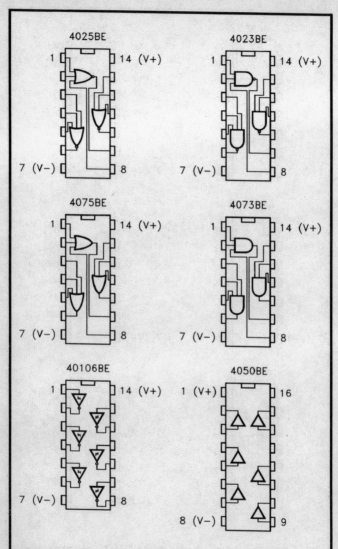

Fig.4.14   Pinout details for some 3 input CMOS gates,
            and buffers/inverters

138

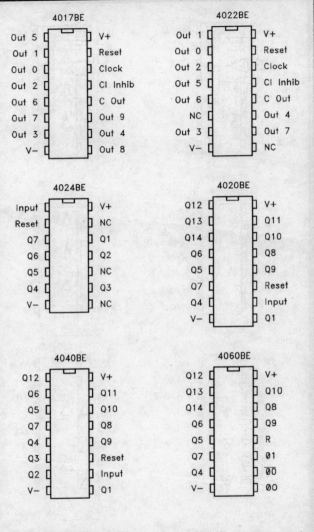

Fig.4.15 Pinout details for some CMOS counters and dividers

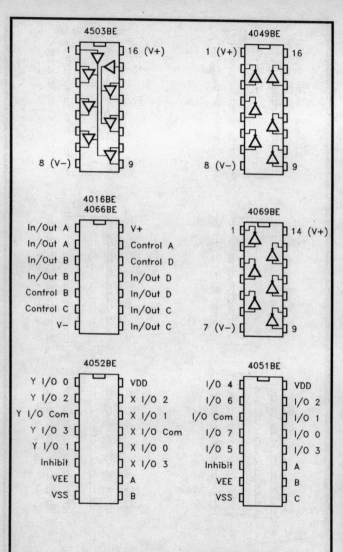

Fig.4.16 Pinout details for some CMOS analogue switches and other devices

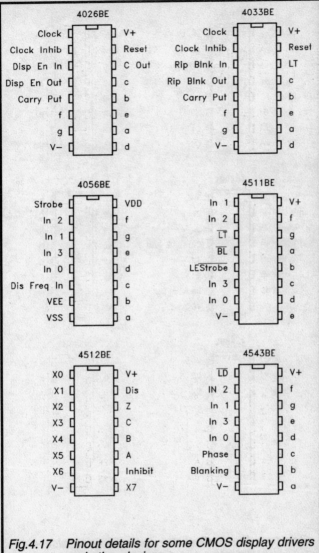

Fig.4.17 Pinout details for some CMOS display drivers and other devices

141

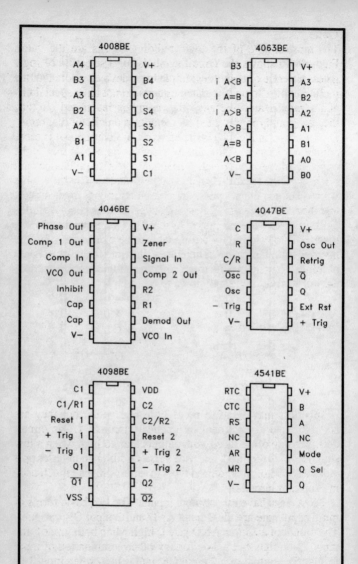

Fig.4.18   Pinout details for miscellaneous CMOS devices

142

Gates

The most simple of the logic building blocks are the gates. Figure 4.19 shows the circuit symbols for a selection of logic gates, plus one or two other simple logic devices. Note that the more complex logic integrated circuits do not have special circuit symbols, and like any other complex integrated circuits, they are simply represented by rectangles on circuit diagrams.

The most simple gate is the not type, or inverter as it is more commonly known. This simply provides an output that is the opposite of the input level. The functions of logic devices are often explained with the aid of a truth table. This is a table which shows every possible combination of input states, together with the output state (or states in the case of a multiple output circuit) produced by each set of input levels. An inverter is too simple for a truth table to be worthwhile, but the inverter truth table shown here does illustrate the basic scheme of things. In general, the more complex a logic block, the more helpful its truth table will prove to be.

Inverter Truth Table

INPUT	OUTPUT
Low	High
High	Low

Inverters may seem to be of little real value, but they are actually used a great deal in practical circuits. Logic circuit designers are often faced with outputs that go high when a low signal level is required, and vice versa. Adding an inverter provides a signal of the required type. Inverters are also much used in oscillator circuits.

Most gates have two or more inputs. The two basic forms of multi-input gate are the 2 input AND and 2 input OR varieties. The output of a 2 input AND gate is high when both input 1 and input 2 are high, but is low for any other combination of input levels. The output of a 2 input OR gate is high when input 1 or input 2 is high, but is low for any other set of input levels. These are the truth tables for 2 input AND and OR gates.

143

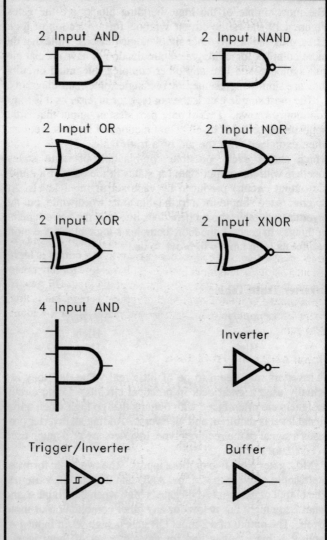

Fig.4.19   Gates, inverter, and buffer circuit symbols

144

2 Input AND Gate Truth Table

INPUT 1	INPUT 2	OUTPUT
Low	Low	Low
Low	High	Low
High	Low	Low
High	High	High

2 Input OR Gate Truth Table

INPUT 1	INPUT 2	OUTPUT
Low	Low	Low
Low	High	High
High	Low	High
High	High	High

The same basic rules apply for a gate that has more than two inputs. For a 3 input AND gate for example, the output is high if input 1, input 2, and input 3 are high, but is low for any other combination of input states. The output of a 4 input OR gate is high if input 1 or input 2 or input 3 or input 4 is high, but is low if none of the inputs are high. This truth table is for a 4 input AND gate.

4 Input AND Gate Truth Table

INPUT 1	INPUT 2	INPUT 3	INPUT 4	OUTPUT
Low	Low	Low	Low	Low
Low	Low	Low	High	Low
Low	Low	High	Low	Low
Low	Low	High	High	Low
Low	High	Low	Low	Low
Low	High	Low	High	Low
Low	High	High	Low	Low
Low	High	High	High	Low
High	Low	Low	Low	Low
High	Low	Low	High	Low
High	Low	High	Low	Low
High	Low	High	High	Low

High	High	Low	Low	Low
High	High	Low	High	Low
High	High	High	Low	Low
High	High	High	High	High

There is a variation on the AND gate called the NAND gate. This is effectively just an AND gate with an inverter added at the output. Consequently, for a given set of input states it will provide the opposite output state to an AND gate. It therefore provides a low output level if all the inputs are high, but a high output level for any other combination of input states.

Similarly, a NOR gate is a variation on the OR gate, and it is effectively an OR gate with an inverter added at the output. Therefore, the output goes low if one or more of the inputs is high, or is high if the inputs are all low. These are the truth tables for 2 input NAND and NOR gates, plus the truth table for a 4 input NAND gate.

2 Input NAND Gate Truth Table

INPUT 1	INPUT 2	OUTPUT
Low	Low	High
Low	High	High
High	Low	High
High	High	Low

2 Input NOR Gate Truth Table

INPUT 1	INPUT 2	OUTPUT
Low	Low	High
Low	High	Low
High	Low	Low
High	High	Low

4 Input NAND Gate Truth Table

INPUT 1	INPUT 2	INPUT 3	INPUT 4	OUTPUT
Low	Low	Low	Low	High
Low	Low	Low	High	High
Low	Low	High	Low	High
Low	Low	High	High	High
Low	High	Low	Low	High
Low	High	Low	High	High
Low	High	High	Low	High
Low	High	High	High	High
High	Low	Low	Low	High
High	Low	Low	High	High
High	Low	High	Low	High
High	Low	High	High	High
High	High	Low	Low	High
High	High	Low	High	High
High	High	High	Low	High
High	High	High	High	Low

There is another variation on the OR gate, and this is the Exclusive OR (XOR) type. The output of an ordinary 2 input OR gate goes high if input 1 or input 2 goes high. However, it also goes high if both input 1 and input 2 go high, rather than just one or the other of them. With an exclusive OR gate the output only goes high if just one input goes high. Any other set of input states results in the output assuming the low state. An exclusive OR gate therefore provides what could reasonably be regarded as a true OR gate function. An exclusive NOR (XNOR) gate provides the same basic function as an exclusive OR gate, but has an inverted output. Exclusive OR and exclusive NOR gates do not seem to be used a great deal in practical applications, but they do have their uses. These are the truth tables for 2 input exclusive OR and exclusive NOR gates, plus the truth table for a 3 input exclusive OR gate.

2 Input XOR Gate Truth Table

INPUT 1	INPUT 2	OUTPUT
Low	Low	Low
Low	High	High
High	Low	High
High	High	Low

2 Input XNOR Gate Truth Table

INPUT 1	INPUT 2	OUTPUT
Low	Low	High
Low	High	Low
High	Low	Low
High	High	High

3 Input XOR Gate Truth Table

INPUT1	INPUT 2	INPUT 3	OUTPUT
Low	Low	Low	Low
Low	Low	High	High
Low	High	Low	High
Low	High	High	Low
High	Low	Low	High
High	Low	High	Low
High	High	Low	Low
High	High	High	Low

Chapter 5

TRANSISTORS, ETC.

Although perhaps not quite such a central part of electronic projects as they once were, having to a large extent been displaced by integrated circuits, transistors are still to be found in many projects. There is certainly no shortage of different types, albeit that some popular devices are available under several different type numbers. In these cases the silicon chip is exactly the same, and it is only the encapsulation or leadout configuration that is different from one type to the next. The basic action of an ordinary bipolar transistor is to provide current amplification, and Figure 5.1 shows the standard transistor test set up. VR1 provides a variable base current to the test transistor, and this is measured by meter ME1. The collector current is monitored using meter ME2. As the base current is varied, the collector current alters in sympathy with it, but the collector current is much larger than the base current. The device therefore provides current gain, and this could be less than 10 times for a low gain device, to as much as a thousand times for a very high gain transistor. The current gain is equal to the collector current divided by the base current.

It is important to realise that the current gain can vary considerably from one device of a particular type number to another device having the same type number. We are used to components with tolerances of about ±1 to 20%, but the tolerance on the current gain of many transistors is more like +150% and −65%. Also bear in mind that the current gain is not constant for any "real world" device, and varies considerably with changes in the collector current. To a much lesser extent it also changes with variations in the collector voltage. In general the current gain reduces as the collector current is reduced, but it also tends to fall away slightly at very high collector currents. A few radio frequency transistors are designed for automatic gain control circuits that use increased bias to reduce the gain on strong signal levels, but these are designed to have an unusual gain characteristic which gives a large reduction in gain as the collector current is increased.

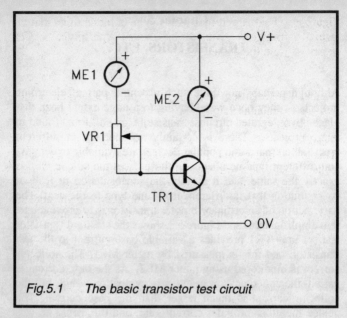

Fig.5.1   The basic transistor test circuit

Parameters

There are numerous parameters associated with transistors, and a brief explanation of some of the more common ones would be in order here.

h_{FE}

This is the d.c. current gain, and should be specified at a particular collector to emitter voltage and collector current. As pointed out previously, the gain of a transistor varies significantly with changes in collector current, and an h_{FE} figure is virtually meaningless unless a collector current is quoted. There is far less variation in gain with changes in collector to emitter voltage, provided this voltage is not extremely low. The absence of a specified collector voltage for the h_{FE} figure is therefore a much less serious omission. The current gains quoted in brief data are usually maximum and minimum figures, and for many devices a wide range of gain levels are acceptable. Something like a gain of between 125 and 900 would not be untypical. Sometimes an "average" or "typical" figure is quoted, and it then needs to be borne in mind that the actual gain of any given device of that type might be well removed from the quoted figure.

h_{fe}

This parameter differs from h_{FE} in that it is not the gain at d.c., but with a small a.c. signal.

V_{CBO}

This is the highest voltage that should be connected across the collector and base terminals with the emitter left open circuit (i.e. with the emitter left unconnected). Exceeding this voltage is likely to result in the component breaking down, and the result of this would almost certainly be to render it unusable.

V_{CEO}

The V_{CEO} rating is similar to the V_{CBO} type, but it is the maximum voltage that should be applied across the collector and emitter terminals with the base left open circuit. This voltage rating is usually somewhat less than the V_{CBO} rating, and is consequently the one that in most applications will determine the maximum usable supply voltage for the device in question.

T_j

T_j is the junction temperature rating of the component. In other words, it is the maximum temperature to which the semiconductor material should be subjected. Exceeding this rating is very likely to result in serious damage to the device, and in extreme cases overheated semiconductors can explode with a loud "crack"! Even using a component just below its T_j rating will probably significantly reduce its reliability. It is important to realise that this rating is the maximum temperature to which the chip of semiconductor material should be allowed to rise. There will not be perfect thermal contact between the chip and the outside of its encapsulation. Consequently, the case temperature must always be well below the T_j rating in order to ensure that the chip also remains comfortably below the relevant temperature. For germanium transistors the T_j figure is often quite low, but for silicon devices it can be (and often is) as high as 175 to 200 degrees Centigrade. Be warned that many power devices run at temperatures that can lead to burnt fingers if you should touch them.

P_{tot}

This is the maximum power rating of the device. As the base current is almost invariably very low in comparison to the collector current, for practical purposes the power dissipated by a transistor can be obtained by multiplying the collector to emitter voltage by the collector current. When dealing with P_{tot} ratings you need to keep in mind that they are the maximum power rating under given sets of operating conditions. For a small signal device, the only operating condition specified might be the ambient temperature, which would normally be 25 degrees Centigrade. Running a transistor at its P_{tot} rating would then be acceptable, provided the ambient temperature would never be more than 25 degrees Centigrade. In practice this could probably not be guaranteed, and the power level would have to be kept substantially below the P_{tot} rating. For power transistors the P_{tot} rating is often given under the assumption that the device is mounted on a very large heatsink, or even a notional infinite heatsink. Under practical operating conditions the P_{tot} power rating may not be usable. Without a heatsink, even 10% of the P_{tot} figure could be sufficient to cause a power device to overheat.

When dealing with P_{tot} ratings remember that you must keep devices within their area of safe operation. In other words, there are often collector voltage and current combinations that give acceptable power ratings, but which will produce local "hot spots" in the semiconductor structure, causing the device to break down and be destroyed. The manufacturers full data should include a graph showing the area of safe operation.

V_{EBO}

When forward biased, the base – emitter terminals of a transistor behave very much like a forward biased diode junction. No significant current flows until the forward threshold voltage of about 0.6 volts is exceeded, after which quite a modest increase in voltage will cause a large current to flow. The base–emitter junction also operates very much like an ordinary diode if it is reverse biased. No significant current flows until the breakdown voltage is reached, and then the device avalanches. This breakdown voltage is quite low for most transistors, with somewhere between 5 and 8 volts being the norm. Like a reverse biased diode or zener diode, exceeding the breakdown voltage will not result in any damage to the device provided the current flow is limited to a safe level.

The V_{EBO} is the reverse breakdown voltage rating of the transistor. It is measured with the collector left open circuit, but connecting the collector into circuit will not usually have any significant affect on this rating. Although this rating might seem of only academic importance, it should be kept in mind that where capacitive coupling is used into the base of a transistor, it can be reverse biased by strong signals of the appropriate type. This is not likely to occur in applications such as audio amplification, but it can easily occur in oscillator circuits. Due to the relatively low breakdown voltage, this can result in some oscillator circuits not operating in the expected manner.

I_C

The I_C rating is the maximum collector current that the component can safely handle. This is normally quoted in the form of the maximum continuous current that can be safely accommodated. However, for some medium power devices intended for switching applications it is a figure for pulsed operation that is quoted. Transistors (and many other semiconductor devices) can readily withstand pulses of high current, and a maximum figure for pulsed operation will therefore be many times higher than the continuous current rating. As a point of interest, pulses of high voltage, even if extremely brief, are virtually certain to damage transistors and most other semiconductor devices.

f_T

This is the transition frequency, which is merely the frequency at which the current gain of the device falls to unity. This is normally quoted for the device when it is operated in the common emitter amplifying mode. This is an important parameter, as it obviously gives a clear indication of the maximum frequency at which the device is likely to provide a useful amount of amplification. Apart from indicating the frequency at which the current gain falls to zero, it also shows the maximum gain that can be achieved at lower frequencies. The maximum gain possible at lower frequencies is equal to the transition frequency divided by the frequency at which a gain figure is required. A device having an f_T of 300MHz for instance, would have a gain of 30 at 10MHz (300MHz divided by 10MHz equals 30). This is an over simplification in that it assumes the transistor has infinite current gain. The gain at low frequencies is obviously limited by the h_{FE} figure of the component.

I_{CEO}

This is merely the leakage current of the transistor. In other words, it is the current that flows between the collector and emitter terminals with the base terminal left open circuit. This parameter is very temperature dependent, but for a silicon device it is normally under one microamp and totally insignificant. It can be quite high for germanium transistors, especially certain power types (although these are now long obsolete).

$V_{CE(sat)}$

The $V_{CE(sat)}$ parameter is more usually just referred to as the saturation voltage. If a strong base current is applied to a transistor connected to operate as a simple common emitter switching stage, the transistor will switch on and provide a very low output voltage. The $V_{CE(sat)}$ rating is a notional minimum collector voltage that can be achieved with the device in this simple switching mode. In reality it is not the lowest collector voltage that can be achieved. If a steadily increasing forward bias is applied to a common emitter switch, the collector voltage will rapidly fall to a low level, and thereafter it will reduce very gradually. The saturation voltage is a potential that is into the part of the transfer characteristic where collector voltage has "bottomed out", but it is not usually the absolute minimum collector voltage that can be achieved.

t_{ON}

When a base current is applied to a transistor it takes a certain amount of time for the device to respond to it and switch on. This is the time specified in the t_{ON} parameter. Like $V_{CE(sat)}$, this is a parameter that is mostly only of importance in logic and other switching applications.

t_{OFF}

t_OFF_

This is similar to t_ON_, but it is the time taken for the transistor to switch off once its base current has been removed. Due to storage effects, the t_OFF_ time for a transistor that has been biased into saturation is much longer than the t_ON_ time.

Amplifying Modes

There are three basic amplifying modes for transistors: the common emitter, common base, and common collector (emitter follower) modes. The common emitter type is probably the most frequently used of these modes, and it is the one which has the most useful characteristics for general use. This mode is shown in Figure 5.2. The name "common emitter" is derived from the fact that the emitter terminal is common to both the input and output signals. R2 is the collector load resistor and R1 provides a base bias to TR1 that results in a collector voltage of about half the supply potential. This is the most basic form of biasing, and there are more complex forms of biasing for this amplifying mode.

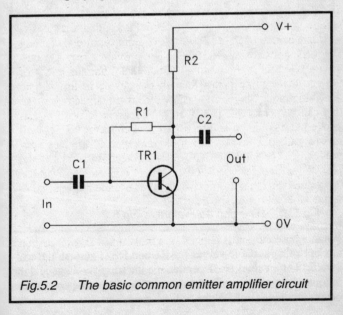

Fig.5.2   *The basic common emitter amplifier circuit*

C1 and C2 provide d.c. blocking at the input and output of the circuit. An a.c. input signal has the effect of causing TR1 to conduct more or less heavily, producing variations in the output voltage. The common emitter mode provides input and output impedance figures that are not usually very different from one another, and are usually several kilohms. The voltage gain is quite high, and at audio frequencies a voltage gain of over 40dB (100 times) is easily achieved. This gives a high level of power gain. The signal undergoes an inversion through a common emitter amplifier.

TR1 is shown as an n.p.n. device in Figure 5.2, but the same configuration will operate properly using a p.n.p. transistor if the supply polarity is reversed, as shown in Figure 5.3. The same is true for the other two amplifying modes.

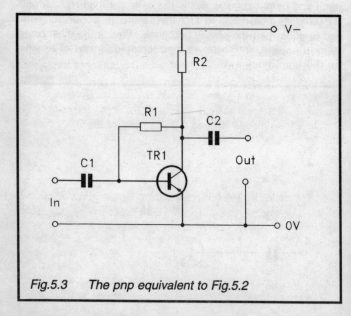

Fig.5.3   The pnp equivalent to Fig.5.2

Selecting suitable values for R1 and R2 is very straightforward. Their values are dependent on the supply voltage and the required quiescent collector current for TR1. Suppose that a supply potential of 9 volts will be used, and that the required

156

collector current is 3 milliamps (0.003 amps). A potential of 4.5 volts is needed across R2 (half the supply voltage). From Ohm's Law the value of R2 can therefore be calculated, and is equal to 4.5 volts divided by 0.003 amps. This works out at 1500 ohms, or 1.5k in other words. Multiplying this value by the typical current gain of TR1 gives a suitable value for R1. With a typical current gain of (say) 200 at a collector current of 3 milliamps, 300k would be a suitable value for R1. The biasing is stabilised to a certain extent by negative feedback, but using a transistor that has a wide h_{FE} range a high degree of accuracy can not be guaranteed.

At audio frequencies the approximate input impedance of the amplifier is given by this formula:

$$Z_{in} = (25/\text{collector I in mA}) \, h_{FE}$$

For our example amplifier we must first divide 25 by the collector current of 3 milliamps. This gives an answer of 8.33, and multiplying this by the h_{FE} of 200 gives an input impedance of 1667 ohms (1.67k). It will be apparent from this that the higher the h_{FE}, the higher the input impedance. Conversely, the higher the collector current, the lower the input impedance.

The approximate voltage gain of the amplifier is given by this formula:

$$V. \text{Gain} = \text{col load } R/(25/\text{col I in mA})$$

Dividing 25 by the collector current again gives an answer of 8.33. Dividing the collector load resistance by this figure then gives a voltage gain of about 180 times.

Common Base
Figure 5.4 shows the circuit diagram for a common base amplifier. This configuration has similarities to the common emitter type. In this case though, the base is decoupled by C2 so that it is held at a fixed voltage and is effectively common to both the input and output terminals. An emitter resistor is added so that the input signal can be coupled to the emitter terminal of TR1. As in the common emitter mode, the input signal

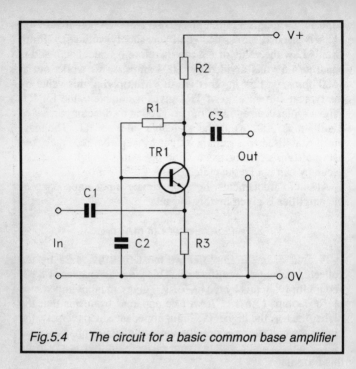

Fig.5.4   The circuit for a basic common base amplifier

produces variations in the base – emitter voltage of the transistor, causing variations in the output voltage. In this case it is the base that is held at a fixed potential and the emitter voltage that is varied, rather than the other way round.

This gives the two types of amplifier very different characteristics though. The voltage gain is very good in the common base mode, but the circuit is really acting as a sort of step-up transformer. The input impedance of the circuit is quite low (typically about 100 to 200 ohms), and the output impedance is quite high. This gives only a low level of power gain. The input and output of the circuit are in-phase, and this contributes to the good performance of this mode at high frequencies.

Emitter Follower
Figure 5.5 shows the circuit diagram for an emitter follower stage. This type of amplifier has a voltage gain that is fraction-

158

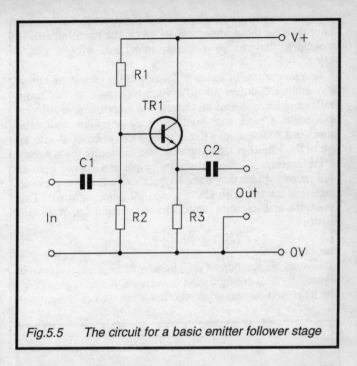

Fig.5.5   The circuit for a basic emitter follower stage

ally less than unity, and it provides no phase shift. An amplifier that provides no voltage amplification may seem to be of no practical value, but the salient point is that it provides a large amount of current amplification. A circuit of this type can therefore be used as a buffer stage to match a high impedance signal source to a much lower impedance load.

An emitter follower stage has an output impedance that is approximately equal to the source impedance divided by the current gain of the transistor. The emitter load resistor (R3) must be chosen to provide a current flow that is at least equal to the required peak output current. The input impedance of the amplifier is roughly equal to the current gain of the transistor multiplied by R3. Accurate biasing will be obtained if R1 and R2 have the same value, and this value is no more than one-tenth of the input impedance to TR1. Unfortunately, this results in R1 and R2 seriously shunting the input of the amplifier,

159

giving the amplifier as a whole an input impedance that is much lower than the input impedance of TR1. The input impedance is equal to the parallel resistance of R1 and R2 (i.e. (R1 × R2)/(R1 + R2)).

This severely reduces the efficiency of the circuit, and these days emitter follower amplifiers are little used in this form. Buffer amplifiers based on operational amplifiers are the normal choice. Operational amplifiers have very high input resistances that enable high value bias resistors to be used with no risk of the amplifier shunting them and impairing the accuracy of the biasing. Common emitter stages are mainly used in applications where they can be direct coupled to the previous stage in a circuit, with C1, R1, and R2 being omitted. This avoids the inefficiencies introduced by the inclusion of the bias resistors.

Darlington Pair

Transistors are sometimes used in pairs in the manner shown in Figure 5.6. This configuration is known as a 'Darlington Pair'. The amplified current of one transistor is fed to the base of the

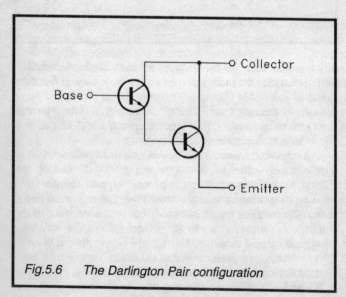

Fig.5.6   The Darlington Pair configuration

second device, giving what is effectively a single transistor having a current gain that is equal to the product of the two individual current gains. In this way an effective current gain of many thousands can be obtained. This configuration is most common in high power emitter follower stages, and power Darlington devices are readily available. Low power Darlington devices are also produced, but this configuration is generally less effective in low power applications, where the input transistor operates at a very low current, making it relatively inefficient.

Type Numbers

Although you could easily get the impression that transistor and diode type numbers are merely thought up at random by the component manufacturers, there is usually some "rhyme and reason" behind them. The amount of information contained in type numbers is strictly limited, and being realistic about it, there is no way large amounts of data about a device could be contained in a short type number. Type numbers often provide a small but useful amount of information though.

Many of the transistors and diodes used by U.K. hobbyists have European Pro Electron type numbers. This method of coding gives some basic information about the type of device concerned. The first letter indicates the material used as the basis of the device, and there are four letters currently in use. These letters, plus the materials they represent, are listed below.

A   Germanium
B   Silicon
C   Gallium Arsenide
R   Compound Materials

The second letter indicates the general type of the device (rectifier, power transistor, etc.). This is a list of the letters and corresponding device types.

A   Small signal diode
B   Rectifier or variable capacitance diode
C   Small signal audio transistor
D   Power Transistor

E	Point contact diode
F	Low power high frequency transistor
G	Diode (oscillator, miscellaneous)
H	Diode (magnetic sensitive)
K	Hall Effect device (open magnetic circuit)
L	High frequency power transistor
M	Hall Effect device (closed magnetic circuit)
N	Opto-Isolator
P	Diode (radiation sensitive)
Q	Diode (radiation producing)
R	Special purpose device
S	Switching device (transistor or diode)
T	S.C.R. or triac
U	High voltage transistor
X	Rectifier or variable capacitance diode
Y	Power rectifier
Z	Zener diode

Devices that have this method of coding include many popular transistors, such as the popular BC series, which are clearly silicon small signal audio types. Some components which have this method of coding have a third letter (e.g. BFY51) which indicates that the device has been designed for the more demanding industrial applications, but does not really seem to be of any great significance. The number which follows the letters would seem to be a serial number, and it therefore gives an indication of how old or recent in design the component happens to be. Note though, that some devices with quite high numbers are the same as older components, but have a different encapsulation.

Gain Groups

A few transistors, and mainly the silicon low power audio types, have a letter at the end of the type number. This indicates the gain grouping of the device. The current gain parameter of many transistors is pretty vague, with minimum and maximum figures of perhaps 125 and 900. Such wide tolerances can make it difficult to design circuits that will give predictable and repeatable results with any given device of that type. To minimise these problems some transistors are available in three gain groups, as well as the standard (ungrouped) version. This applies mainly to devices in the BC107/8/9 and BC177/8/9 series, and their derivatives (BC547, BC557, etc.). The gain-grouped devices have an "A", "B", or "C" suffix. These indicate the following generally accepted gain ranges.

A	110 to 220
B	200 to 450
C	420 to 800

Some transistors which have 2N series type numbers are also gain-grouped. Probably the best known example is the 2N2926, which was extremely popular at one time. The gain groupings for these devices are indicated by coloured spots, as detailed in this list

Red	55 to 100
Orange	90 to 180
Yellow	150 to 300
Green	235 to 470

A few transistors which have Pro Electron type numbers have a "K" or "L" suffix letter. This has nothing to do with gain grouping, and indicates that a different leadout configuration has been used. This method seems to have fallen from favour, and these days it would seem to be normal for devices having different leadout configurations to be given new type numbers, rather than modified versions of old ones.

JEDEC Codes

JEDEC stands for "Joint Electronic Device Engineering Councils), and it is an American organisation. Devices having JEDEC type numbers accordingly have their origins in the U.S.A. These components are quite common in the U.K. though, and the JEDEC 1N and 2N series type numbers will be familiar to many readers (e.g. 1N4148 and 2N2926). These type numbers provide very little information about the components, but do have some significance. The number at the start of a JEDEC code is equal to one less than the number of leadout wires that the component possesses. It therefore gives some indication of the device type, as detailed here.

1	A diode or other two lead device
2	A bipolar, unijunction, or field effect transistor, or some form of S.C.R.
3	A dual gate f.e.t. or other four lead type
4 or 5	Opto-isolator

The second digit is always an "N", and is followed by a number having up to four digits. Devices are numbered in sequence as they are registered, and the type numbers give a rough guide to the relative ages of devices. A very few devices having "A" suffixes are available, and this simply indicates that they are improved versions of the original device. For instance, the 2N706A is an improved version of the earlier 2N706, and has a substantially different set of parameters.

JIS Codes
JIS (Japanese Industry Standard) type numbers would seem to be something of a rarity in U.K. electronic component catalogues. Japanese transistors, diodes, etc. do not seem to find their way into many designs for the U.K. home constructor. The first digit of the type number indicates the number of leadout wires in much the same way as the initial digit in a JEDEC type number (i.e. the number is one less than the number of leadout wires). The next two digits are letters which indicate the general type of the component. This is a list of the letters and the types of component they represent.

SA	PNP transistor or Darlington pair (high frequency)
SB	PNP transistor or Darlington pair (low frequency)
SC	NPN transistor or Darlington Pair (high frequency)
SD	NPN transistor or Darlington pair (low frequency)
SE	Diodes
SF	SCRs (thyristors)
SG	Gunn diodes
SH	Unijunction transistors
SJ	P channel f.e.t.s (including power f.e.t.s)
SK	N channel f.e.t.s (including power f.e.t.s)
SM	SCRs (triacs)

SQ	Light emitting diodes
SR	Rectifiers
SS	Signal diodes
AT	Avalanche diodes
SV	Variable capacitance diodes
SZ	Zener diodes

The final part of the type number is a serial number of up to four digits in length. You may occasionally encounter JIS devices which have an extra letter at the end of the type number. This apparently indicates that the device has been approved by a Japanese organisation. An "N" for instance, indicates that it has been approved by a broadcasting station. Note that on actual devices the first two digits often seem to be absent. This is not particularly important since the first digit can be ascertained by counting the leadout wires, and the second digit is invariably an "S". There is only a risk of confusion if you fail to realise that the type number is of the abridged JIS variety.

Manufacturers Digits
Not all semiconductors conform to any of these methods of numbering, and some are sold under manufacturers own type numbers. The first two to four letters then indicate the manufacturer concerned, plus (possibly) some general indication as to the type of device concerned or its encapsulation. This is a list of the main manufacturers and their code letters.

MJ	Motorola (metal cased power transistor)
MJE	Motorola (plastic cased power transistor)
MPS	Motorola (plastic cased low power transistor)
MRF	Motorola (high frequency or microwave transistor)
RCA	RCA
RCS	RCA
TIP	Texas Instruments (plastic cased power transistor)
TIPL	Texas Instruments (planar power transistor)
TIS	Texas Instruments (low power transistor)
ZT	Ferranti
ZTX	Ferranti

Tables

These tables provide basic data for a wide range of bipolar transistors.

Transistor Characteristic Tables
Small–medium Power Audio Transistors

Device	Type	V_{CEO}	h_{FE}	$P_{TOT}(mW)$	$I_C(mA)$	Case
BC107	npn	45	110-450	300	100	TO18
BC108	npn	20	110-800	300	100	TO18
BC109	npn	20	110-800	300	100	TO18
BC117	npn	120	40 typ	500	20	TO39
BC142	npn	60	20 min	800	800	TO39
BC143	pnp	60	25 min	800	800	TO39
BC169C	npn	20	650 typ	300	50	TO92
BC171	npn	45	110-450	300	200	TO92a
BC177	pnp	45	125-500	300	100	TO18
BC178	pnp	25	125-500	300	100	TO18
BC179	pnp	25	240-500	300	100	TO18
BC182L	npn	50	100-480	300	200	TO92
BC183L	npn	30	80-400	300	200	TO92
BC184L	npn	30	125 min	300	200	TO92
BC212L	pnp	50	60-300	300	200	TO92
BC213L	pnp	30	80-400	300	200	TO92
BC214L	pnp	30	140-600	300	200	TO92
BC239	npn	45	290 typ	360	100	TO92h
BC327	pnp	45	100-600	625	500	TO92b
BC337	npn	45	100-600	625	500	TO92b
BC441	npn	60	40-250	1000	2000	TO39
BC461	pnp	60	40-250	1000	2000	TO39
BC547	npn	45	520 typ	500	100	TO92a
BC548	npn	30	520 typ	500	100	TO92a
BC549	npn	30	520 typ	500	100	TO92a
BC550	npn	45	520 typ	500	200	TO92a
BC557	pnp	45	240 typ	500	100	TO92a
BC558	pnp	30	240 typ	500	100	TO92a
BC559	pnp	30	240 typ	500	100	TO92a
BC560	pnp	45	240 typ	500	200	TO92a
BCY70	pnp	40	300 typ	360	200	TO18
BCY71	pnp	45	100-400	360	200	TO18
BFX29	pnp	60	125 typ	600	600	TO5
BFX30	pnp	65	90 typ	600	600	TO5
BFX84	npn	60	110 typ	800	1000	TO5
BFX85	npn	60	140 typ	800	1000	TO5
BFX87	pnp	50	125 typ	600	600	TO5
BFX88	pnp	40	125 typ	600	600	TO5
BFY50	npn	35	110 typ	800	1000	TO5

Device	Type	V_{CEO}	h_{FE}	$P_{TOT}(mW)$	$I_C(mA)$	Case
BFY51	npn	30	125 typ	800	1000	TO5
BFY52	npn	20	142 typ	800	1000	TO5
ZTX107	npn	50	240 typ	300	100	E-line
ZTX108	npn	30	240 typ	300	100	E-line
ZTX109	npn	30	410 typ	300	100	E-line
ZTX300	npn	25	150 typ	300	500	E-line
ZTX500	pnp	25	150 typ	300	500	E-line
ZTX650	npn	45	200 typ	1500	2000	E-line
ZTX651	npn	60	200 typ	1500	2000	E-line
ZTX750	pnp	45	200 typ	1500	2000	E-line
ZTX751	pnp	60	200 typ	1500	2000	E-line
2N697	npn	40	75 typ	600	500	TO5
2N706	npn	20	20 min	300	100	TO18
2N1711	npn	30	200 typ	800	1000	TO5
2N1893	npn	80	80 typ	800	500	TO5
2N2219	npn	30	200 typ	800	800	TO5
2N2905	pnp	40	100-300	600	600	TO5
2N2906	pnp	40	80 typ	400	600	TO18
2N2907	pnp	40	200 typ	400	600	TO18
2N2926	npn	18	55-435	200	100	TO98
2N3702	pnp	25	60-300	300	200	TO92
2N3703	pnp	30	30-150	300	200	TO92
2N3704	npn	30	100-300	360	800	TO92
2N3705	npn	30	50-150	360	800	TO92
2N3706	npn	20	315 typ	360	800	TO92
2N3707	npn	30	250 typ	250	30	TO92
2N3708	npn	30	360 typ	250	30	TO92
2N3711	npn	30	420 typ	250	30	TO92
2N3903	npn	40	100 typ	300	200	TO92b
2N3904	npn	40	100-300	310	200	TO92b
2N3905	pnp	40	50 typ	310	200	TO92b
2N3906	pnp	40	100-300	310	200	TO92b

The gain figures are mostly quoted at one or two milliamps for small devices, and a much higher current of around 100 milliamps for the medium power devices. The 2N3707 is designed for low current applications, and the gain is for a collector current of 100 microamps. The BC109, BC549, BC550, BC169, BC559, and BC560 are high gain low noise audio devices. The 2N697, 2N706, 2N2906, 2N2907, 2N2219, 2N2905, ZTX650, ZTX651, ZTX750, and ZTX751 are all high speed switching devices. All type are silicon transistors.

Small–medium Power R.F. Transistors

Device	Type	V_{CEO}	h_{FE}	P_{TOT} (mW)	I_C (mA)	f_r (MHz)	Case
BF115	npn	30	40 typ	145	30	230	TO72a
BF173	npn	25	38 typ	260	25	350	TO72a
BF180	npn	20	13 typ	150	200	325	TO72
BF182	npn	20	75 typ	145	30	325	TO72
BF184	npn	20	75 typ	145	30	150	TO72a
BF185	npn	20	34 typ	145	30	110	TO72a
BF200	npn	20	13 typ	150	20	325	TO72
BF254	npn	20	115 typ	220	30	260	TO92z
BF255	npn	20	67 typ	220	30	260	TO92z
BF257	npn	160	25 typ	500	100	55	TO39
BF258	npn	250	25 typ	800	100	55	TO39
BF259	npn	300	25 typ	500	100	90	TO39
BF337	npn	225	20 typ	800	100	80	TO39
BF420	npn	300	40 min	830	25	60	TO92a
BF421	pnp	300	40 min	830	25	60	TO92a
BF494	npn	20	115 typ	300	30	260	TO92k
BFR39	npn	80	50 typ	800	1000	100	TO92a
BFR40	npn	60	75 typ	800	1000	100	TO92a
BFR41	npn	50	100 typ	800	1000	100	TO92a
BFR79	pnp	80	50 typ	800	1000	100	TO92a
BFR80	pnp	60	75 typ	800	1000	100	TO92a
BFR81	pnp	50	100 typ	800	1000	100	TO92a
BFR90A	npn	15	90 typ	180	25	5000	SOT-37
BFY90	npn	15	52 typ	200	50	1850	TO72
BSX20	npn	15	80 typ	360	500	500	TO18
MPSH10	npn	25	60 typ	350	20	650	TO92e
2N2222A	npn	40	200 typ	500	800	300	TO18
2N2369A	npn	15	40 min	360	200	500	TO18
2N3866	npn	30	105 typ	5000	400	700	TO5

Due to the increased use of f.e.t.s, integrated circuits, and surface mount devices in radio frequency circuits, the range of readily available high frequency transistors seems to have drastically shrunk in recent years. Some of the devices listed here might therefore be difficult to obtain. All types are silicon transistors.

Power Transistors

Device	Type	V_{CEO}	h_{FE}	$P_{TOT}(W)$	$I_C(A)$	$f_T(MHz)$	Case
BD131	npn	45	20 min	15	3	60	TO126
BD132	pnp	45	20 min	15	3	60	TO126
BD135	npn	45	40-250	12.5	1.5	50	TO126
BD136	pnp	45	40-250	12.5	1.5	75	TO126
BD139	npn	80	100 typ	8	1	250	TO126
BD140	pnp	80	100 typ	8	1	75	TO126
BC437	npn	45	40 typ	36	4	3	TO126
BD438	pnp	45	40 typ	36	4	3	TO126
BD539C	npn	100	30 typ	45	5	–	P1b
BC540C	pnp	100	30 typ	45	5	–	P1b
BD679	npn	80	2200 typ	40	6	0.06	P1b
BD680	pnp	80	2200 typ	40	6	0.06	P1b
BD711	npn	100	25 typ	75	12	3	P1b
BD712	pnp	100	25 typ	75	12	3	P1b
BD911	npn	100	30 typ	90	15	3	P1b
BD912	pnp	100	30 typ	90	15	3	P1b
BU208	npn	1500	2.25 min	12.5	5	7	TO3
MJ2501	pnp	80	1000 typ	150	10	1	TO3
MJ2955	npn	60	45 typ	150	15	4	TO3
MJ3001	npn	80	1000 typ	150	10	1	TO3
MJE340	npn	300	150 typ	20	0.5	20	TO126
MJE350	pnp	300	150 typ	20	0.5	20	TO126
TIP31A	npn	60	25 typ	40	3	3	P1b
TIP32A	pnp	60	25 typ	40	3	3	P1b
TIP33A	npn	60	75 typ	80	10	3	P3c
TIP34A	pnp	60	75 typ	80	10	3	P3c
TIP41A	npn	60	50 typ	65	5	3	P1b
TIP42A	pnp	60	50 typ	65	5	3	P1b
TIP121	npn	80	1000 min	65	5	1	P1b
TIP122	npn	100	5000 typ	65	5	5	P1b
TIP126	pnp	80	1000 min	65	5	1	P1b
TIP127	pnp	100	5000 typ	65	5	5	P1b
TIP142	npn	100	3000 typ	125	10	–	P3c
TIP147	pnp	100	3000 typ	125	10	–	P3c
TIP2955	pnp	70	45 typ	90	15	2	P3c
TIP3055	npn	70	45 typ	90	15	2	P3c
2N3054	npn	55	25 typ	29	4	1	TO3
2N3055	npn	60	45 typ	115	15	0.8	TO3
2N3772	npn	60	30 typ	150	20	0.8	TO3
2N3773	npn	140	40 typ	150	16	0.2	TO3
2N6609	pnp	140	40 typ	150	16	0.2	TO3

Note that the V_{CEO} figure for the BU208 is a non-repetitive peak value. Devices having h_{FE} figures of 1000 or more are power Darlington transistors. All types are silicon transistors. Many power devices have low f_T figures, and in some cases may not provide full gain over the entire audio band.

Figure 5.7 shows leadout details for a wide range of small bipolar transistors. Figure 5.8 provides leadout details for a number of power types. As is the convention, both show underside views of the components.

FETs

Originally there was only one type of field effect transistor (f.e.t.), and this was the junction gate (Jfet). These have now been joined by various types of MOSFET, including power types such as VMOS and HMOS transistors. All these devices can operate in amplifying modes that are analogous to the common base, common emitter, and common collector modes. However, the terminals of field effect transistors are called the gate, source, and drain. The f.e.t. amplifying modes are therefore the common gate, common source, and common drain (source follower) types.

An essential difference between bipolar and field effect transistors is that whereas bipolar devices are current operated, field effect devices are voltage operated. In other words, it is the voltage applied to the gate of a field effect transistor that is of importance, not the gate current. The input resistances of field effect transistors are so high that the gate currents are extremely low indeed. The input resistance of a Jfet is usually in excess of one thousand megohms, while that of a MOSFET can often exceed one million megohms! While the input impedance at low frequencies is similarly high, it reduces substantially at medium and high frequencies due to the input capacitance. This is typically about 10p, but in the common source amplifying mode this is effectively multiplied by the gain of the device due to the Miller Effect.

Jfets and some MOSFETs are depletion mode devices. With a bipolar transistor the device is normally switched off, and it is turned on by applying a forward bias. A depletion mode field effect device is switched on quite hard with zero gate bias, and in normal operation it is given a reverse bias so that it can

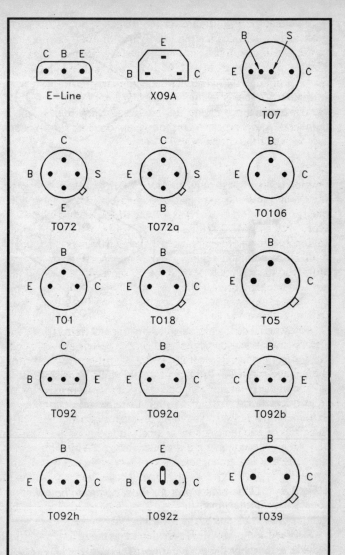

Fig.5.7   Base views for a wide range of small transistors

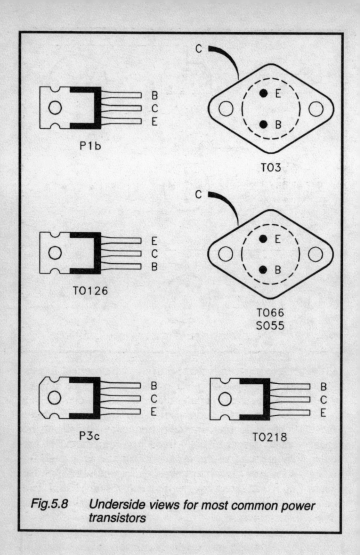

Fig.5.8 Underside views for most common power transistors

provide reasonably linear operation. This reverse bias is normally provided via a resistor in the source circuit, plus another resistor to bias the gate to the 0 volt supply rail, as in Figure 5.9. This is very much like the bias circuits used in valve circuits,

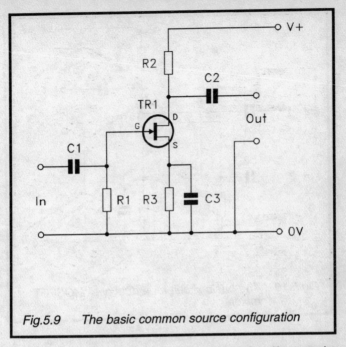

Fig.5.9   The basic common source configuration

and in some respects the characteristics of field effect transistors are more like those of valves than those of bipolar devices.

Jfets are perhaps less popular than they once were, but they are still used in both audio and radio frequency circuits. MOSFETs are little used in audio frequency equipment, but appear in many pieces of radio frequency equipment. In particular, they are used in the r.f. and mixer stages of high frequency (h.f.), very high frequency (v.h.f.), and ultra high frequency (u.h.f.) radio receiving equipment. Good MOSFET r.f. and mixer stages can provide excellent large signal handling and noise performance.

As their name implies, dual gate MOSFETs have two gate terminals. Although one might reasonably expect that this would result in the output simply responding to the sum of the two input voltages, it does not work this way in practice. The gain from one gate to the output is controlled by the voltage at the other gate. In a radio receiver mixer stage application, feed-

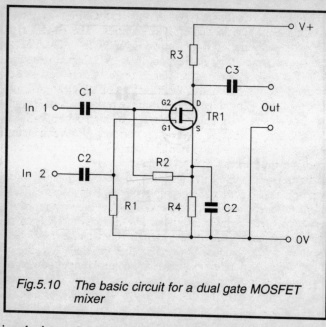

Fig.5.10   The basic circuit for a dual gate MOSFET mixer

ing the input signal to one gate and the oscillator signal to the other gate therefore gives the required complex mixing action needed to provide the heterodyne effect. Figure 5.10 shows the basic configuration for a dual gate MOSFET mixer. If a dual gate MOSFET is utilized in an r.f. stage, the input signal can be applied to one gate, with the other gate being given either a fixed bias level or being fed with a variable bias from the automatic gain control (a.g.c.) circuit.

Dual gate MOSFETs are depletion mode devices. Most of the single gate type now available seem to be "enhancement" mode MOSFETs, which are more like bipolar devices than the standard depletion mode devices. They are normally switched off, and require a forward bias to bring them into conduction. Being field effect devices, it is still the input voltage rather than the gate current that is of importance. It is transistors of this type that are used in CMOS logic integrated circuits incidentally. Many enhancement mode MOSFETs are designed for use in switching applications.

174

There are two main types of power MOSFET available, which are the VMOS and HMOS varieties. The HMOS type are often just referred to as "power MOSFETs". The VMOS transistors derive their name from their "V" shaped structure. Whereas ordinary field effect transistors have "on" resistances of about 100 to 500 ohms, the structure of VMOS transistors enables them to produce drain to source resistances of 2 ohms or less. This permits them to control quite high currents. Some devices are capable of controlling currents of several amps. HMOS devices have a different structure, but have broadly similar characteristics to VMOS devices.

Both types of power f.e.t. tend to be significantly more expensive than good quality bipolar power transistors capable of handling comparable power levels. Also, they are probably more easily damaged than bipolar power transistors. They do have a few distinct advantages though. Perhaps the most obvious one is the enormous power gain they provide. A swing of a few volts at a negligible current can control output powers of a hundred watts, or even more. Switching speeds are very fast for power devices. Thermal stability is another factor in their favour. As mentioned previously in this chapter, bipolar devices have to be operated in their so-called area of safe operation. Certain combinations of collector current and voltage cause what is termed "secondary breakdown", which results in local "hot spots" in the semiconductor structure, and the destruction of the device. With virtually all power f.e.t.s, any source voltage and current combinations that provide acceptable power dissipation figures are acceptable.

FET Parameters
Obviously field effect transistors are very different to bipolar transistors in many respects, and accordingly they have a largely different set of parameters. This is a list of the main parameters, together with a brief explanation of each one.

f_T
This is basically the same as the f_T rating of a bipolar device, but it is, of course, the unity gain bandwidth in the common source amplifying mode (the equivalent of the bipolar common emitter mode).

P_{TOT}

P_T is an exact equivalent to P_{TOT} for a bipolar transistor (i.e. the maximum permissible power rating).

V_p

V_p is the pinch-off voltage. This is the reverse gate to source voltage needed to switch off a depletion mode field effect transistor. Obviously this parameter is not applicable to enhancement mode devices.

V_{GS}

This is the maximum permissible gate to source voltage, and is roughly analogous to V_{EBO} for a bipolar transistor. However, no avalanche effect is obtained with field effect devices. Note that some power f.e.t.s (particular the VMOS variety) are protected by a zener diode against excessive gate voltages. In these cases the V_{GS} rating is the avalanche voltage of the zener protection diode.

V_{DG}

V_{DG} is the maximum permissible drain to gate voltage, and is roughly equivalent to V_{CBO} for a bipolar transistor.

V_{DS}

The maximum drain to source voltage, and the f.e.t. equivalent of V_{CEO}.

C_{iss}

This is the input capacitance with the component used in the common source amplifying mode.

g_m

The g_m rating is the small signal common source transconductance. As the f.e.t. method of gain measurement, this is roughly equivalent to h_{FE} for a bipolar transistor, but is only a rough equivalent. Remember that with a field effect transistor we are not dealing in terms of input and output current, but with input voltage and output current. This parameter is therefore a measurement of how much the output current changes with a given variation in the gate voltage. Conductance is similar to resistance, but is essentially the inverse of it. It is a measure of how well something conducts electricity instead of a measurement of how much it resists a current flow. The unit of measurement used for conductance and transconductance was called the "mho", but it is now called the "siemens". The g_m formula of current divided by voltage is the inverse of that used to calculate resistance using Ohm's Law. If a f.e.t. had a transconductance rating of 12 mS (12 milli siemens, or twelve thousandths of a siemens), a change in the gate voltage of one volt would result in the drain current changing by 12 milliamps.

$V_{GS(th)}$

This is the gate threshold voltage, and it only applies to enhancement mode devices. It is the forward bias voltage at which the device begins to switch on. This is similar to the 0.6 volts or thereabouts needed before a silicon bipolar transistor will start to turn on, but for enhancement mode f.e.t.s the turn on threshold voltage is generally about 0.8 to two volts.

I_{DSS}

I_{DSS} is the enhancement mode f.e.t. equivalent to leakage (I_{CEO}) in a bipolar transistor. It is the drain current that flows with zero gate bias voltage. Even for power f.e.t. devices this figure is normally quite low (a few microamps or less), and it is not normally of any significance in practice.

I_{GSS}

This parameter is the gate leakage current. It is merely the gate current that flows for a given gate voltage. Due to the very high input resistance of f.e.t.s this rating is normally no more than a nanoamp or two, but it can be a few microamps for power f.e.t.s under worst case conditions.

I_D

This parameter is normally only specified for power f.e.t.s, and it is the maximum permissible drain current.

I_{Dss}

This is the drain current that flows through a depletion mode f.e.t. that is subjected to zero gate to source voltage. Using this figure and the g_m parameter it is possible to calculate the drain current for other gate bias levels. However, the tolerances on both g_m and I_{Dss} ratings are often quite high. The tolerance on the I_{Dss} parameter in particular is usually quite large, with the maximum figure being perhaps as much as ten times higher than the minimum one. This makes accurate biasing of many depletion mode f.e.t.s a difficult task.

t_{on}
This is simply the switch on time for the device.

t_{off}
The t_{off} rating is the switch off time for the device. Unlike bipolar switch on/off time ratings, the turn on and turn off delays for f.e.t.s are often the same.

R_{DS}
This is simply the drain to source resistance with the device fully switched on.

$V_{DS(on)}$
This could reasonably be regarded as the power f.e.t. equivalent to saturation voltage. It is the drain to source voltage with the device heavily forward biased and conducting a specified current.

In the "Type" column "N" is for N channel, P is for P channel, "Jfet" is a junction gate f.e.t., DG-MOS is a dual gate MOSFET, and DG-GAS is a dual gate gallium arsenide device. The BFW10 is a low noise device for low frequency applications, and the 3SK134 is a very low noise high frequency device (noise figure of 1.3dB at 900MHz). Many of the older types (e.g. 3N140 and 40673) are now difficult to obtain, and expensive. They are not recommended for use in new designs.

FET Characteristics

Small Signal FETs

Device	Type	V_{DS}	g_m (mS)	P_{TOT} (mW)	I_{Dss} (mA)	Case
BF244A	N-Jfet	30	4.5 typ	360	25	TO92d
BF244B	N-Jfet	30	3-6.5	360	25	TO92d
BFW10	N-Jfet	30	3.2 typ	300	20	TO12
MPF102	N-Jfet	25	1.6 typ	200	20	TO92c
J109	N-Jfet	25	17 typ	360	40	TO92c
J112	N-Jfet	35	6 typ	360	5	TO92c
2N3819	N-Jfet	25	2-6.5	200	20	TO92d
2N3820	P-Jfet	20	0.8-5	200	15	TO92d
2N3823E	N-Jfet	30	1.8 min	250	20	TO106f
2N4303	N-Jfet	30	2 min	300	10	TO106f
2N4416	N-Jfet	30	–	300	5	TO72k
2N4220	N-Jfet	30	–	300	0.5	TO72j
2N4861	N-Jfet	30V	–	360	8	TO18n
2N5457	N-Jfet	25	1-5	200	5	TO92c
2N5458	N-Jfet	25	1.5-5.5	200	9	TO92c
2N5459	N-Jfet	25	2-6	200	16	TO92c
2N5460	P-Jfet	40	1	310	5	TO92p
2N5461	P-Jfet	40	–	310	2	TO92p
3N140	DG-MOS	20	10 typ	330	30	TO72f
3SK88	DG-MOS	20	17 typ	200	6	FET-37
3SK124	DG-GAS	10	30 typ	200	40	FET-37
40673	DG-MOS	20	12 typ	330	35	TO72f

Power MOSFETS

Device	Type	V_{DS}	g_m (mS)	P_{TOT} (mW)	I_{Dss} (mA)	Case
BUZ10	N-PMOS	50	3000 typ	70	20	P1d
BUZ31	N-PMOS	200	5000 typ	75	12.5	P1d
IRF540	N-PMOS	100	10S typ	125	27	P1d
IRF630	N-PMOS	200	4800 typ	75	9	P1d
IRF640	N-PMOS	200	10S typ	125	18	P1d
IRF740	N-PMOS	400	7000 typ	125	10	P1d
IRF830	N-PMOS	500	3250 typ	75	4.5	P1d
IRF840	N-PMOS	500	6500 typ	125	8	P1d
VN10KM	N-VMOS	60	200 typ	1	0.5	TO92d
VN46AF	N-VMOS	40	250 typ	12.5	2	P1c
VN66AF	N-VMOS	60	250 typ	12.5	2	P1c
VN67AF	N-VMOS	60	250 typ	15	2	P1c
VN88AF	N-VMOS	80	250 typ	12.5	2	P1c
2SJ48	P-PMOS	120	1000 typ	100	7	TO3v
2SJ49	P-PMOS	140	1000 typ	100	7	TO3v
2SJ50	P-PMOS	160	1000 typ	100	7	TO3v

2SJ83	P-PMOS	160	1000 typ	100		7	FPACK
2SJ114	P-PMOS	200	1000 typ	100		8	TO3w
2SJ160	P-PMOS	120	1000 typ	100		7	TO3w
2SJ161	P-PMOS	140	1000 typ	100		7	TO3w
2SJ162	P-PMOS	160	1000 typ	100		7	TO3w
2SK133	N-PMOS	120	1000 typ	100		7	TO3v
2SK134	N-PMOS	140	1000 typ	100		7	TO3v
2SK135	N-PMOS	160	1000 typ	100		7	TO3v
2SK227	N-PMOS	160	1000 typ	100		7	TO3v
2SK1056	N-PMOS	120	1000 typ	100		7	TO3w
2SK1057	N-PMOS	140	1000 typ	100		7	TO3w
2SK1058	N-PMOS	160	1000 typ	100		7	TO3w

In the "Type" column "N" indicates an N channel device, "P" indicates a P channel device, "VMOS" indicates a VMOS device, and "PMOS" is for an HMOS device or some other form of power MOSFET.

Figure 5.11 shows leadout details for a wide range of low lower field effect transistors, and Figure 5.12 shows base views for a number of common power types. Transistors intended for surface mounting are now starting to appear in component catalogues, and Figure 5.13 shows leadout details for two common forms of surface mount transistor (one f.e.t. and one bipolar type).

Unijunctions

Although unijunction transistors were very popular at one time, they have been largely superseded by integrated circuit oscillators and timers. They are little used these days, and are bordering on obsolescence. They can still be obtained, but few are now available, and supplies may well "dry-up" in the not too distant future. Unijunctions are not something that could be recommended for use in new designs.

Unijunction transistors have little in common with bipolar or field effect types. They have three leadout wires and are housed in standard transistor encapsulations, but that is where the similarities end. Unijunctions are not used in amplifiers, and can not provide gain. They have two base terminals and an emitter terminal. Unijunctions are normally used in a relaxation oscillator, as in the example circuit of Figure 5.14. Here C1 charges by way of R1 until a certain voltage is reached, and then TR1 "fires" and rapidly discharges C1. When C1 is almost

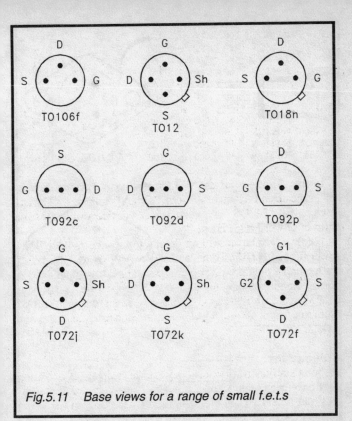

Fig.5.11   Base views for a range of small f.e.t.s

fully discharged TR1 switches off again, C1 commences to charge via R1 once more, and so on. This gives a high impedance non-linear sawtooth waveform at the emitter of TR1, and low impedance pulse signals at the base 1 and base 2 terminals.

As one would expect, the parameters in data sheets for unijunction transistors are totally different to those for ordinary bipolar types. This is a list and brief explanation of the main ones.

V_{BB}

The maximum permissible base 1 to base 2 voltage.

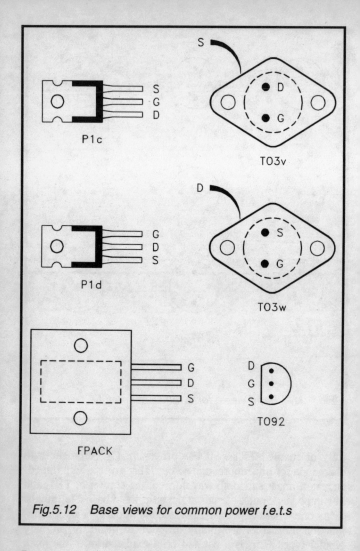

Fig.5.12   Base views for common power f.e.t.s

I_P

This is the peak point current, which is the minimum emitter current needed to trigger the device. If the timing resistor value in a unijunction relaxation oscillator is made too high, this

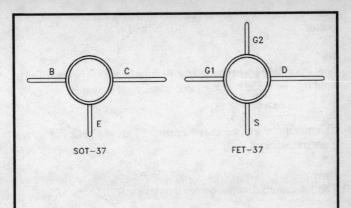

Fig.5.13　Leadout details for two types of surface mount transistor

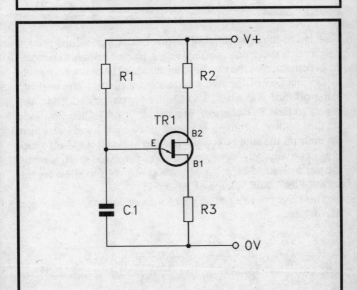

Fig.5.14　The circuit for a basic unijunction relaxation oscillator

current will not be reached and oscillation will not occur.

I_V

I_V is the valley point current, or the minimum current needed to hold the device in the triggered state in other words.

I_E

The maximum emitter current rating. This is a peak rating, not a continuous one.

P_{TOT}

The maximum dissipation for the device.

R_{BB}

The base 1 to base 2 resistance.

n

This is the intrinsic stand-off ratio. Under static conditions a unijunction transistor is effectively a pair of resistors connected in series across the two base terminals. The emitter connects to the junction of the two resistors via a diode. The intrinsic stand-off ratio is the base 1 to emitter resistance divided by the base 1 to base 2 resistance. The device "fires" when the diode at the emitter terminal becomes forward biased, and this depends on the supply voltage and the intrinsic stand-off ratio. It is approximately equal to the supply voltage multiplied by the intrinsic stand-off ratio, plus about 0.6 volts to allow for the forward threshold voltage of the diode.

This table provides basic data for three common unijunction transistors.

Device	V_{BB}	V_{EB}	$R_{BB}(k)$	n	$I_P(\mu A)$	Case
TIS43	35	30	4-9.1	0.55-0.82	5	TO92e
2N2646	35	30	4.7-9.1	0.56-0.75	5	TO18u
2N4871	35	30	4-9.1	0.7-0.85	5	TO92g

Figure 5.15 provides leadout details for these three unijunction transistors.

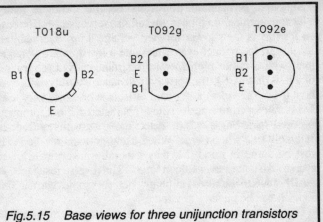

Fig.5.15   Base views for three unijunction transistors

Diodes

Rectifiers and zener diodes are covered in Chapter One in the
section dealing with power supply circuits, and will not be dealt
with again here. However, the subject of ordinary diodes will
be dealt with here. I am sometimes asked to explain where the
dividing line is drawn between rectifiers and diodes. Rectifiers
are used in power supplies and other high current applications,
whereas diodes are used in low current circuits. There is no
rigidly defined operating current that separates diodes from
rectifiers, but it seems to be generally accepted that a component that can handle currents of one amp or more is a rectifier,
and one that can not handle currents of at least something
approaching this figure is a diode. Here we will only consider
devices that can deal with currents of up to a few hundred
milliamps.

A silicon diode requires a forward potential of about 0.6
volts before it will start to conduct significantly. Only a mar-
ginally higher voltage is then sufficient to make it conduct
heavily. In some applications this forward voltage drop of
about 0.6 to 0.7 volts is of no consequence, but sometimes it is
a major drawback. The reverse resistance of silicon diodes is
very high, and is generally in the region of 100 megohms or
more.

185

Although germanium transistors became obsolete many years ago, germanium diodes are still in everyday use. The reason for this is their lower forward voltage drop. Germanium diodes start to conduct even with quite a low forward voltage, albeit with a rather high forward resistance. As the forward voltage is increased, the forward resistance steadily falls. At about 0.1 to 0.2 volts the forward resistance becomes very low. This is still far from a perfect diode characteristic, but for many purposes, including a.m./f.m. detection, a germanium diode is preferable to a silicon type. When using germanium diodes it must be borne in mind that they generally have much lower reverse resistances than silicon types. The reverse resistance is usually several hundred kilohms, but for some germanium diodes it can be under 100 kilohms.

There have been various attempts to produce "improved" diodes having lower forward voltage drops, but the only other type in widespread use is the Schottky diode. This is the same type of diode that is used within 74LS** series TTL chips. It is a type of silicon diode, but with a lower forward conduction threshold voltage that is typically about 0.4 volts. In other words, the forward conduction characteristic of a Schottky diode is roughly half way between that of a germanium diode and a silicon type. Schottky diodes are very fast in operation, and many will operate at frequencies of several gigahertz (i.e. several thousand megahertz).

Most diodes have a coloured band around one end of the case to denote the cathode (+) leadout wire. A few types have multiple coloured bands, and these are a form of colour coding which show the component's type number. In practice you are only likely to encounter 1N4148 diodes which have this type of marking. The "4148" part of the type number is marked using the method of coding adopted for bands one and two of resistor colour codes. The yellow band should be thicker than the others, and this band is next to the cathode leadout wire (Fig.5.16).

Parameters

This is a list of the parameters you are likely to encounter in short-form data sheets for diodes, complete with a brief explanation of each one.

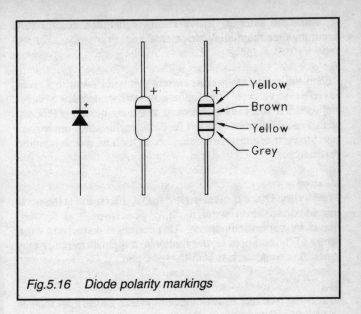

Fig.5.16   Diode polarity markings

PIV
This is the "peak inverse voltage". As its name suggests, this is the peak reverse bias voltage that should be applied to the device. Semiconductors tend to be quite voltage conscious, and even slightly exceeding this voltage rating for a very brief period of time could result in the device being damaged. Remember that the peak voltage in an a.c. signal is about 1.41 times its r.m.s. level.

I_f
The I_f rating is the maximum average current that should be allowed to flow with the component forward biased. As already mentioned, semiconductor devices are easily damaged by excessive voltages, but they are much more tolerant of high current pulses. A diode that can handle an average forward current of (say) 50 milliamps may well be able to handle pulses of up to about ten times this figure, provided they are suitably brief. However, where high peak currents are involved

it would be safer to use a rectifier that can comfortably accommodate these high currents.

I_R

This is the maximum reverse current that will flow with a given reverse bias voltage. This figure is normally quoted at a potential which is equal to or very close to the component's PIV rating. For silicon diodes it is usually a fraction of a microamp, but for germanium types it can be as high as a few hundred microamps.

V_F drop

The V_F drop figure is often quoted for rectifiers, and is the maximum voltage drop through the device when it is forward biased by a specified current. This current is sometimes the I_f rating of the component, but it may be a typical operating current. This could be just a milliamp or two.

T_{rr}

This is the recovery time of the component, or the time it takes to switch off in other words. Fast recovery diodes generally have T_{rr} times of around 10 to 40ns.

T_j

The T_j rating is the maximum safe junction temperature. This is not the same as the maximum safe case temperature, and the latter is several degrees lower than the T_j rating.

This table gives brief data for some common types of diode.

Device	Type	PIV	I_F(mA)	Applications
AA119	G Point Contact	45	35	AM/FM detector
BA244	S	20	100	Fast switching
BA481	Schottky barrier	4	30	UHF mixer
BAR28	Schottky barrier	70	–	Fast - low V drop
BAT85	Schottky barrier	30	200	AM/FM detector
BAW62	S Epitaxial Planar	75	100	Fast logic
BAX13	S Whiskerless	50	75	Fast switching
BAX16	S Whiskerless	150	200	General purpose
BY206	S Double diff	350	400	Switching PSUs
HSCH1001	Schottky barrier	60	15	Fast - low V drop
OA47	G Gold bonded	25	110	Low V drop switching

OA90	G Point contact	30	10	AM/FM detector
OA91	G Point contact	115	50	General purpose
OA95	G Point contact	115	50	General purpose
OA200	S Alloy junction	50	80	General purpose
OA202	S Alloy junction	150	40	General purpose
ZS120	S Alloy junction	50	250	General purpose
1N914	S Whiskerless	100	75	Fast switching
1N914B	S Whiskerless	75	75	Low V drop
1N916	S Whiskerless	50	250	Low cap switching
1N4148	S Whiskerless	100	75	Fast switching
1S921	S Diffused	100	200	General purpose

In the "Type" column "S" indicates a silicon device, and "G" indicates a germanium diode. Schottky diodes are a form of silicon diode.

SCRs

A silicon controlled rectifier (SCR) is a switching device. Unlike an ordinary rectifier, it does not normally conduct between its cathode and anode terminals when they are forward biased. An SCR has an additional terminal called the "gate", and it is only when this is forward biased with respect to the cathode that the device is triggered into conduction. The voltage drop through the device is rather higher than that through a normal silicon rectifier, being about twice as high at around 1.2 to two volts. Once an SCR, or thyristor as they are popularly known, has been triggered, it will remain in a state of conduction until the anode to cathode current falls below a certain level. Therefore, removing the gate bias will not switch off a thyristor if the anode to cathode current is above this hold-on threshold level. There are actually a few special types called "gate turn-off" thyristors that can be switched off via the gate, but these are something of a rarity.

The gate pulse only needs to be quite short, with a one microsecond pulse generally being sufficient to trigger a thyristor reliably. The gate current needed to provide triggering varies considerably from one type to another. Some of the older devices require as much as 20 to 30 milliamps to guarantee proper triggering. This still represents a respectable level of gain for what are essentially power devices that are normally used to control currents of around one to 10 amps. However, some modern thyristors will trigger reliably at gate currents of well under one milliamp.

There are a number of important thyristor parameters to be found in data on these devices. A list of the main parameters, together with a short explanation of each one, is provided below.

V_r

This is the maximum reverse voltage rating of the device (i.e. the maximum voltage with the anode taken negative of the cathode). This is usually a peak voltage, whereas a.c. voltages are generally given as r.m.s. figures. The peak voltage is equivalent to about 1.41 times the r.m.s. level (e.g. about 324 volts for the 230 volt U.K. mains supply).

V_f

This is the maximum forward voltage rating (i.e. the maximum voltage with the anode taken positive of the cathode).

I_f

I_f is the maximum forward current that the device can handle. It is either an average or r.m.s. figure, and the peak level can safely be very much higher than this.

V_g

The V_g rating is the maximum gate voltage that will be needed in order to trigger the component. This is typically about 1 volt or so.

I_g

This is the maximum gate current required to trigger the component. For older and higher power devices this figure can be quite high, at about 10 to 30 milliamps. For many recent thyristors it is much lower than this, at typically only about 200 microamps.

I_{hm}

I_{hm} is the maximum holding current. In other words, this is the minimum current that must be kept passing through the device in order to prevent it from switching off. It is not the current required in order to guarantee that the device will switch off (which is likely to be very much lower than the I_{hm} figure).

V_fm

As pointed out previously, there is a voltage drop through a thyristor that is about 1.2 volts or so. V_{fm} is the maximum forward voltage drop with the device operating at maximum current.

This table provides basic data for some common thyristors.

Device	$V_r(V)$	$I_f(A)$	$I_g(mA)$	$V_g(V)$	$I_{hm}(mA)$	Case
BT109	500	4	10	2	3	TO220
BT149B	200	0.64	0.2	0.8	5	TO92t
TAG84	600	0.64	0.2	0.8	5	TO92t
C106D	400	2.5	0.2	0.8	3	TO220
C106M	600	2.5	0.2	0.8	3	TO220
C116D	400	5	20	1.5	40	TO220
C126D	400	7.5	30	1.5	40	TO220
C126M	400	7.5	20	1.5	40	TO220
CF106D	400	3.2	0.2	1	5	TO220
CF106M	600	3.2	0.2	1	5	TO220
CP106D	400	1.25	0.2	1	5	TO92t
CP106M	600	1.25	0.2	1	5	TO92t
2N1599	400	1	10	3	–	TO5
2N6399	800	7.5	30	1.5	40	TO220

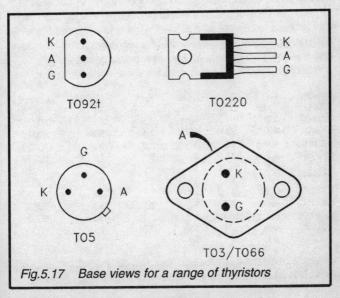

Fig.5.17   Base views for a range of thyristors

Base views for a range of thyristors (including those above) are provided in Figure 5.17.

Triacs and Diacs

Triacs and diacs are a developments of the basic s.c.r. In fact a diac could be regarded as a step backwards, as it is a simple two terminal device. It is effectively a thyristor that has no gate terminal. Although this may seem a bit useless, with no way of triggering the device, this is not the case. If the forward voltage across the anode and cathode of a thyristor is made large enough, the device will break down and it will effectively trigger itself into conduction. A diac is designed to have quite a low breakdown voltage of typically about 30 to 35 volts (but much lower on some recent types). The main use of a diac is to trigger a thyristor or triac when the gate voltage reaches a certain level. This method is much used in lamp dimmers and other a.c. power control applications. Note that a diac is bidirectional, and will operate with an input voltage of either polarity.

A triac has similar characteristics to a thyristor, but it is fully bidirectional. It can be triggered by a gate signal of either polarity, and can control a signal of either polarity. A triac can therefore be used to control an a.c. load. This is in fact possible with a thyristor, but only with the aid of a rectifier circuit to ensure that it is fed with signals of the appropriate polarity.

This table provides basic data for some common triacs.

Device	$V_r(V)$	$I_f(A)$	$I_g(mA)$	$V_g(V)$	$I_{hm}(mA)$	Case
C206D	400	3	5	2	30	TO220
C226D	400	8	50	2.5	60	TO220
C236D	400	12	50	2.5	50	TO220
C246D	400	16	50	2.5	50	TO220
CF206D	400	4	5	2	15	TO220
CF206M	600	4	5	2	15	TO220
CF225D	400	8	20	2	20	TO220
CF225M	600	8	20	2	20	TO220
CP206D	400	1.5	8	2.5	30	TO92r
CP206M	600	1.5	8	2.5	30	TO92r
SC146D	400	10	50	2.5	75	TO220
2N6073	400	4	30	2.5	70	TO220

Figure 5.18 shows base views for a range of triacs.

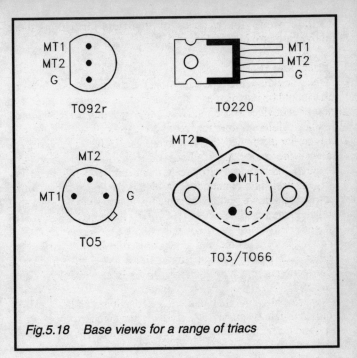

Fig.5.18   Base views for a range of triacs

Chapter 6

MISCELLANEOUS DATA

This chapter provides a large amount of miscellaneous data, including radio, MIDI, and computer related data.

Short Wave Bands
There are thirteen short wave broadcast bands. These are listed below, together with the frequency span of each one.

Short Wave Broadcast Bands

Band	Frequency Range
120 Metres	2.3MHz to 2.498MHz
90 Metres	3.2MHz to 3.4MHz
75 Metres	3.95MHz to 4.0MHz
60 Metres	4.75MHz to 5.06MHz
49 Metres	5.95MHz to 6.2MHz
41 Metres	7.1MHz to 7.3MHz
31 Metres	9.5MHz to 9.9MHz
25 Metres	11.65MHz to 12.05MHz
22 Metres	13.6MHz to 13.8MHz
19 Metres	15.1MHz to 15.6MHz
16 Metres	17.55MHz to 17.9MHz
13 Metres	21.45MHz to 21.85MHz
11 Metres	25.67MHz to 26.1MHz

There are currently nine short wave amateur bands, and these plus their frequency spans are listed below. Incidentally, the 160 metre band is popularly known as "topband", but the other bands seem to lack any nickname of this type.

Short Wave Amateur Band

Metres	Frequency Range
Metres	1.8MHz to 1.85MHz (2.0MHz)
80 Metres	3.5MHz to 3.8MHz (4.0MHz)
40 Metres	7.0MHz to 7.1MHz (7.3MHz)
29.5 (30) Metre	10.1MHz to 10.15MHz

20 Metres	14.0MHz to 14.35MHz
16.5 (17) Metres	18.068MHz to 18.168MHz
15 Metres	21.0MHz to 21.45MHz
12 Metres	24.89MHz to 24.99MHz
10 Metres	28MHz to 29.7MHz

In some countries, including the U.K., 160 metres has an upper limit of 2.0MHz, whereas in other countries it ends at 1.85MHz. Similarly, in some countries the 80 metre band extends right up to 4.0MHz, and the 40 metre band extends to 7.3MHz. Note that in the U.K. these bands end at the 3.8MHz and 7.1MHz limits. Some of these bands are not exclusively for amateur use, and other stations (such as maritime types) will be found within these bands. It is mainly the low frequency bands where these other transmissions are to be found.

There are three V.H.F. amateur bands, as detailed here.

Band	Frequency Range
6 Metres	50 to 52MHz
4 Metres	70.025 to 70.5MHz
2 Metres	144 to 146MHz

These are the band limits for the U.H.F. amateur bands.

Band	Frequency Range
70 Centimetres	432 to 440MHz
23 Centimetres	1240 to 1325MHz
13 Centimetres	2300 to 2450MHz

CB Frequency Allocations

The 27MHz citizens band has 40 channels covering frequencies from 27.6025MHz to 27.99125MHz (10kHz channel spacing). The maximum transmitter power is 4 watts, with a maximum e.r.p. of 2 watts. The only form of modulation permitted is f.m., and the maximum deviation is ±2.5kHz. The aerial is a base loaded rod or wire no longer than 1.5 metres long, and the transmitter output power must be reduced by at least 10dB if the aerial is more than 7 metres above ground level.

Channel	Frequency (MHz)
1	27.60125
2	27.61125
3	27.62125
4	27.63125
5	27.64125
6	27.65125
7	27.66125
8	27.67125
9	27.68125
10	27.69125
11	27.70125
12	27.71125
13	27.72125
14	27.73125
15	27.74125
16	27.75125
17	27.76125
18	27.77125
19	27.78125
20	27.79125
21	27.80125
22	27.81125
23	27.82125
24	27.83125
25	27.84125
26	27.85125
27	27.86125
28	27.87125
29	27.88125
30	27.89125
31	27.90125
32	27.91125
33	27.92125
34	27.93125
35	27.94125
36	27.95125
37	27.96125
38	27.97125
39	27.98125
40	27.99125

The 934MHz citizens band has 20 channels with 50kHz channel spacing, but this may eventually be reduced to 25kHz. The frequency range covered is from 934.025MHz to 934.975MHz. The maximum transmitter output power is 8 watts, and the maximum e.r.p. is 3 watts if the aerial is built-in, or 20 watts if it is not. The aerial may have up to four elements, but none must be more than 170 millimetres long. If the aerial is mounted more than 10 metres above ground level the transmitter output power must be reduced by at least 10dB. Only f.m. is permitted, and the maximum deviation is ±5kHz.

Channel	Frequency (MHz)
1	934.025
2	934.075
3	934.125
4	934.175
5	934.225
6	934.275
7	934.325
8	934.375
9	934.425
10	934.475
11	934.525
12	934.575
13	934.625
14	934.675
15	934.725
16	934.775
17	934.825
18	934.875
19	934.925
20	934.975

Frequency – Wavelength Conversion

MHz	Metres
1	300
1.1	272.7
1.2	250
1.3	230.8
1.4	214.3
1.5	200
1.6	187.5
1.7	176.5
1.8	166.6
1.9	157.9
2.0	150
2.5	120
3	100
3.5	86
4	75
4.5	66.6
5	60
5.5	54.5
6	50
6.5	46.2
7	42.9
7.5	40
8	37.5
8.5	35.3
9	33.3
9.5	31.6
10	30
11	27.27
12	25
13	23.08
14	21.43
15	20
16	18.75
17	17.65
18	16.88
19	15.79
20	15

21	14.29
22	13.64
23	13.04
24	12.5
25	12
26	11.54
27	11.11
28	10.71
29	10.34
30	10

Frequencies outside the range of this table can be accommodated without too much difficulty. For example, a frequency of 100Mz is ten times higher than 10MHz, and it will therefore have a wavelength only one tenth as long. The wavelength at 10MHz is 30 metres, and the wavelength at 100MHz will therefore be 3 metres. Frequency to wavelength conversion is quite easy anyway, and to convert from megahertz to metres simply divide 300 by the frequency (e.g. 300 divided by 4MHz equals 75 metres). To convert kilohertz to metres divide 300,000 by the frequency (e.g. 300,000 divided by 100kHz equals 3000 metres).

Wavelength to frequency conversion is equally straightforward. Dividing 300 by the wavelength in metres gives an answer in megahertz, or dividing 300,000 by the wavelength in metres gives an answer in kilohertz. For instance, 150 metres is equivalent to 2MHz (300 divided by 150 equals 2MHz), or 2000kHz (300,000 divided by 150 = 2000kHz).

Amateur Abbreviations
Amateur abbreviations were originally used to enable messages in Morse code to be sent in a more compact form. They are still used for Morse code communications, but many (XYL for example) are now used much more generally by the radio amateur fraternity. This list gives details of many of the more common amateur abbreviations.

Code	Meaning
ABT	About
AGN	Again

ALC	Automatic level control
AM	Amplitude modulation
ANI	Any
ANT	Antenna
ARS	Amateur radio society
BC	Broadcast
BCI	Broadcast interference
BCNU	Be seeing you
BFO	Beat frequency oscillator
BK	Break
BT	Battery
BW	Bandwidth
B4	Before
CANS	Headphones
CCT	Circuit
CK	Check
CLG	Calling
CO	Crystal oscillator
CQ	Request for someone to respond to a transmission
CONDX	Conditions
CUAGN	See you again
CUL	See you later
CUD	Could
CW	Continuous wave (Morse code)
DE	From
DET	Detector (demodulator)
DF	Direction finder
DSB	Double sideband
DX	Long distance or otherwise difficult communication
ERE	Here
ES	And
FB	Fine business
FD	Field day
FM	Frequency modulation
FR	For
FONE	Telephony (voice communication)
GA	Go ahead or good afternoon
GB	Goodbye
GE	Good evening
GG	Going

GLD	Glad
GM	Good morning
GND	Ground (earth)
GUD	Good
HI	Laughter, high spirits
HPE	Hope
HR	Hear hear
HRD	Heard
HV	Have
HW	How
ID	Identification
IF	Intermediate frequency
KHZ	Kilohertz
LID	Bad operator
MNI	Many
MS	Meteor scatter
MSG	Message
MHZ	Megahertz
ND	Nothing doing
NW	Now
OB	Old boy
OG	Old girl
OM	Old man
OP	Operator
OT	Old timer
PA	Power Amplifier
PSE	Please
R	Everything received correctly
RPT	Report
RX	Receiver
SA	Say
SED	Said
SIGS	Signals
SRI	Sorry
SSB	Single sideband
SUM	Some
SWL	Short wave listener
TKS	Thanks
TMW	Tomorrow
TNX	Thanks

TT	That
TU	Thank you
TVI	Television interference
TX	Transmitter
U	You
UR	You are
VFO	Variable frequency oscillator
VXO	Variable crystal oscillator
VY	Very
WID	With
WKD	Worked
WL	Will
WUD	Would
WX	Weather
XYL	Wife (Ex young lady)
YF	Wife
YL	Young lady
73	Best wishes
88	Love and kisses

Q Codes

The Q codes are not exclusively used by radio amateurs, and are used generally in the field of radio communications. They were originally designed to streamline Morse code communications, but are used more generally these days. They are used to ask questions, as in the list provided here, but can also be used as an answer or an instruction. Some have become general terms. For example, QRP can mean "shall I reduce power", and it is also used by radio amateurs as a general term for low-power operation.

Code	Meaning
QRA	What is the name of your station?
QRB	What is your approximate distance from my station?
QRH	Does my frequency fluctuate?
QRI	Is my note good?
QRK	Are you receiving well? (also used by amateurs as an abbreviation for money!)
QRL	Are you busy?

QRM	Is my signal contaminated with man-made interference?
QRN	Is my signal subject to atmospheric interference?
QRO	Do you wish me to increase power? (also used as an abbreviation for high power operation)
QRP	Do you wish me to reduce power? (also used as an abbreviation for low power operation)
QRQ	Shall I send faster?
QRS	Shall I send slower?
QRT	Shall I stop sending? (also used to signify that a station is closing down)
QRV	Are you ready?
QRX	Shall I wait?
QRZ	Who is calling me?
QSB	Does my signal vary in strength? (also used as an abbreviation for signal fading)
QSL	Did you copy that? (also the name of a card sent as confirmation of a contact, or to acknowledge a reception report)
QSO	A contact with another station
QSP	Will you relay this message to ......?
QSV	Shall I send a series of Vs?
QSZ	Shall I send each group of words twice?
QSY	Shall I change frequency?
QTH	What is your location? (also used as a general abbreviation for the address from which a radio amateur operates his or her station)

SINPO

SINPO is a form of brief reception report, and it rates five aspects of the signal on a scale of one to five. These five aspects are signal strength (S), interference (I), noise (N), propagation disturbance (P), and overall readability (O). Rating details for all five of these are listed here.

Signal Strength

1	Only just audible
2	Poor
3	Fair

| | 4 | Good |
| | 5 | Excellent |

Interference

	1	Extremely bad
	2	Severe
	3	Moderate
	4	Slight
	5	None

Noise

	1	Extremely bad
	2	Severe
	3	Moderate
	4	Slight
	5	None

Propagation Disturbance

	1	Extremely bad
	2	Severe
	3	Moderate
	4	Slight
	5	None

Overall Rating

	1	Unreadable
	2	Poor
	3	Fair
	4	Good
	5	Excellent

Baudot Codes

Baudot coding is the standard method of sending data via RTTY (radio teletype) links. This method of coding is used by both amateur and commercial RTTY stations. Amateur stations mainly use transmission rate of 45 baud (45.45 to be precise), or occasionally 50 baud. The most common frequency shift for amateur RTTY is 170 hertz. Baudot codes are five bit types, and are sent with one start bit plus one or one and a half stop bits. Five bit coding gives 32 different codes, which is not enough for a full alpha-numeric character set plus punctuation marks. This shortcoming is overcome in two ways. Firstly, only upper case characters are supported. Secondly, a shift system is used, with one character set containing letters and common punctuation marks, and the other containing numbers and further punctuation marks. This table provides details of all the Baudot codes.

DECIMAL	HEX	LETTERS	FIGURES
0	00	Not used	Not used
1	01	E	3
2	02	Line feed	Line feed
3	03	A	–
4	04	Space	Space
5	05	S	Bell or '
6	06	I	8
7	07	U	7
8	08	Return	Return
9	09	D	$
10	0A	R	4
11	0B	J	' or bell
12	0C	N	,
13	0D	F	! or %
14	0E	C	:
15	0F	K	(
16	10	T	5
17	11	Z	"
18	12	L	)
19	13	W	2
20	14	H	ú or #
21	15	Y	6
22	16	P	0
23	17	Q	1
24	18	O	9
25	19	B	?
26	1A	G	& or +
27	1B	Figures	Figures
28	1C	M	.
29	1D	X	/

| 30 | 1E | V | ; |
| 31 | 1F | Letters | Letters |

("Letters" and "Figures" are the two shift characters)

Morse Code

A dot is equal to one unit of time, and a dash lasts three units. The space between dots/dashes forming a character is one unit of time. The space between characters lasts three units of time, and the space between two words equals five units of time.

A	.-
B	-...
C	-.-.
D	-..
E	.
F	..-.
G	--.
H	....
I	..
J	.---
K	-.-
L	.-..
M	--
N	-.
O	---
P	.--.
Q	--.-
R	.-.
S	...
T	-
U	..-
V	...-
W	.--
X	-..-
Y	-.--
Z	--..
1	.----
2	..---
3	...--

4	· · · · —
5	· · · · ·
6	— · · · ·
7	— — · · ·
8	— — — · ·
9	— — — — ·
0	— — — — —
Apostrophe	· — — — — ·
Bracket	— · — — · —
Break sign	— · · · —
Comma	— — · · — —
End of message	· — · — ·
End of work	· · · — · —
Error	· · · · · · · ·
Full stop	· — · — · —
Hyphen	— · · · · —
Inverted commas	· — · · — ·
Question mark	· · — — · ·
Understood	· · · — ·
Wait	· — · · ·

ASCII Codes

Virtually all modern computers use a character set that is closely based on the ASCII (American Standard Code for Information Interchange) set. These are seven bit codes, giving a maximum of 128 different characters. Many computers use the eighth bit for additional, non-standard codes (i.e. code numbers from 128 to 255 are often used for non-standard graphics characters, etc.). This table provides details of the standard ASCII codes.

DECIMAL	HEX	BINARY	CHARACTER
0	00	0000000	NULL
1	01	0001	SOH
2	02	0010	STX
3	03	0011	ETX
4	04	0100	EOT
5	05	0101	ENQ
6	06	0110	ACK

7	07	0111	BEL
8	08	1000	BS
9	09	1001	HT
10	0A	1010	LF
11	0B	1011	VT
12	0C	1100	FF
13	0D	1101	CR
14	0E	1110	SO
15	0F	1111	SI
16	10	0010000	DLE
17	11	0001	DC1
18	12	0010	DC2
19	13	0011	DC3
20	14	0100	DC4
21	15	0101	NAK
22	16	0110	SYN
23	17	0111	ETB
24	18	1000	CAN
25	19	1001	EM
26	1A	1010	SUB
27	1B	1011	ESC
28	1C	1100	FS
29	1D	1101	GS
30	1E	1110	RS
31	IF	1111	US
32	20	0100000	[SPACE]
33	21	0001	!
34	22	0010	"
35	23	0011	[HASH]
36	24	0100	$
37	25	0101	%
38	26	0110	&
39	27	0111	'
40	28	1000	(
41	29	1001	)
42	2A	1010	*
43	2B	1011	+
44	2C	1100	,
45	2D	1101	-
46	2E	1110	.

47	2F	1111	/
48	30	0110000	0
49	31	0001	1
50	32	0010	2
51	33	0011	3
52	34	0100	4
53	35	0101	5
54	36	0110	6
55	37	0111	7
56	38	1000	8
57	39	1001	9
58	3A	1010	:
59	3B	1011	;
60	3C	1100	<
61	3D	1101	=
62	3E	1110	>
63	3F	1111	?
64	40	1000000	@
65	41	0001	A
66	42	0010	B
67	43	0011	C
68	44	0100	D
69	45	0101	E
70	46	0110	F
71	47	0111	G
72	48	1000	H
73	49	1001	I
74	4A	1010	J
75	4B	1011	K
76	4C	1100	L
77	4D	1101	M
78	4E	1110	N
79	4F	1111	0
80	50	1010000	P
81	51	0001	Q
82	52	0010	R
83	53	0011	S
84	54	0100	T
85	55	0101	U
86	56	0110	V

87	57	0111	W
88	58	1000	X
89	59	1001	Y
90	5A	1010	Z
91	5B	1011	[
92	5C	1100	\
93	5D	1101	]
94	5E	1110	^
95	5F	1111	[L.ARROW]
97	60	1100000	_
98	61	0001	a
99	62	0010	b
100	63	0011	c
101	64	0100	d
102	65	0101	e
103	66	0110	f
104	67	0111	g
105	68	1000	h
106	69	1001	i
107	6A	1010	j
108	6B	1011	k
109	6C	1100	l
110	6D	1101	m
111	6E	1110	n
112	6F	1111	o
113	70	1110000	p
114	71	0001	q
115	72	0010	r
116	73	0011	s
117	74	0100	t
118	75	0101	u
119	76	0110	v
120	77	0111	w
121	78	1000	x
122	79	1001	y
123	7A	1010	z
124	7B	1011	{
125	7C	1100	[double dash]
126	7D	1101	}
127	7E	1110	~

MIDI Codes

MIDI is an acronym for "musical instruments digital interface". MIDI is a form of serial interface, and it is very similar to the standard RS232C and RS423 computer serial interfaces. MIDI uses a word format of one start bit, eight data bits, one stop bit, and no parity. It is a form of asynchronous serial interface, which means that the timing signals are sent on the same line as the data. In fact the only synchronisation signal is the start bit at the beginning of each byte. This indicates the commencement of a byte of data, and that the voltage on the connecting lead must be tested at regular intervals thereafter until a full byte of data has been received. It does not ensure that the transmitting and sending devices are properly synchronised while each byte of data is sent. This is achieved by sending/receiving data at a standard rate. For MIDI the standard "baud" rate is 31250 baud, or 31.25 kilobaud if you prefer. This simply means that data is transmitted at a rate of 31250 bits per second (assuming a continuous flow of data).

RS232C and RS423 interfaces use different voltages to represent logic 0 and logic 1 levels, but MIDI is different in that it uses a 5 milliamp current loop. In other words, the current is switched on to indicate one logic level, and switched off to represent the other logic state. This is done due to the use of opto-isolators at each input, which keep items of equipment in the system electrically isolated from one another. This eliminates the risk of damage occurring when two or more items of equipment are connected together, due to their chassis being at different voltages. It also helps to reduce the risk of "hum" loops being produced when a number of instruments and other equipment are connected together. Finally, it also helps to avoid having electrical noise coupled from a computer into the audio stages of an instrument.

The standard MIDI connector is a 5 way 180 degree DIN type. Figure 6.1 provides connection details for the three different types of MIDI port. A THRU port is a form of output, and it simply provides a replica of the signal received at the IN socket. Note that the shield of the cable is left unconnected at

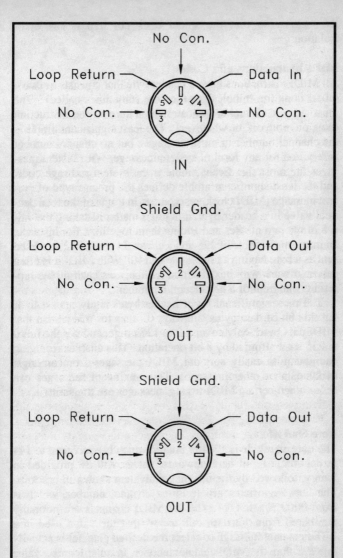

Fig.6.1   Connection details for the three types of MIDI
           port

IN sockets, so that the shield does not bypass the opto-isolation.

MIDI Instructions and Codes

All MIDI instructions have a header byte that consists of two 4 bit sections (or "nibbles" as they are sometimes called). The most significant nibble indicates the nature of the instruction (note on, note off, or whatever). The least significant nibble is the channel number in most messages, but no channel number is required for any form of system message. With system messages the most significant nibble is the system message code, and the least significant nibble defines the precise type of system message (MIDI clock, reset, etc.). In terms of the total decimal value in a header byte, it is just a matter of taking the values of the two nibbles and adding them together. For instance, an instruction nibble of 128 and a channel value of 12 would be sent as a byte having a total value of 140. With MIDI it is often easier to work with hexadecimal numbers, as each nibble represents one digit of a hexadecimal number.

The most significant bit of header bytes is always set to 1, but this bit of data bytes is always 0. It is for this reason that MIDI data bytes only cover a 0 to 127 range, and not the full 0 to 255 span afforded by 8 bit operation. This enables receiving equipment to easily sort out MIDI messages from amongst MIDI data of other messages. This mixing of messages can occur when certain MIDI timing messages are transmitted.

Note On/Off

The note on nibble is 1001 in binary, which is equivalent to 144 in decimal. From here onwards, values will be provided in binary, followed by the decimal equivalent shown in brackets. The least significant nibble is the channel number, which is from 0000 (0) to 1111 (15). As MIDI channels are normally numbered from 1 to 16, this means that the value used in a MIDI channel message to select the desired channel is actually one less than the MIDI channel number. In other words a value of 0 selects channel 1, a value of 1 selects channel 2, and so on. The note on message is followed by two data bytes, which are the note number and the velocity value.

214

Note off messages have 1000 (128) as the most significant nibble, and the channel number as the least significant nibble. The header byte is followed by two data bytes, which are again the note number and velocity value. A note on message having a velocity value of 0 can be used as an alternative form of note off message.

Key Pressure
Overall key pressure (sometimes called "channel" pressure) has the instruction nibble 1101 (208) and is followed by a single data byte. Polyphonic key pressure has 1010 (160) as the instruction nibble, and is followed by two data bytes. These are the note value first, and the pressure value second. For both types of message the least significant nibble of the header byte contains the channel number.

Control Change, Etc.
The control change header byte has 1011 (176) as the most significant nibble in the header byte, while the least significant nibble is the channel number value. The header is followed by two data bytes, which are the control number followed by its new value. Controls from 0 to 31 are paired with controls from 32 to 63 (respectively), and these operate as high resolution continuous controls. Each pair of seven bit numbers are combined to give a single 14 bit value. The lower numbered controller always provides the most significant bits, with the higher numbered control providing the seven least significant bits. In terms of decimal numbers, the range available is from 0 to 16383. Note that it is quite acceptable to change only one or other of the controls in a pair, and a change to one does not necessitate a change to the other.

Control numbers from 64 to 95 are used for switch type controls. Originally only control values of 0 (off) and 127 (on) were valid with these, and other control values were ignored. An amendment to the specification now has values from 0 to 63 as off, and from 64 to 127 as on. Control numbers from 96 to 121 are, as yet, unassigned. These are available for future expansion, and may be assigned specific functions in due course.

The remaining control numbers (122 to 127) are used for mode changes and similar functions. These have a value of 0 for the control value byte, apart from controls 122 (local on/off) and 126 (mono on). Local control is a standard on/off switch type control, and is from 64 to 127 to activate the keyboard (or whatever), and 0 to 63 to switch it off. When mono mode is switched on, the control value selects the number of voices to be set to mono mode (a value of 0 sets all the instrument's voices to mono mode). The MIDI specification only calls for mono mode channels to be contiguous, but some instruments have special modes which allow them to be assigned to any desired channels.

Pitch Wheel

The pitch wheel header byte has 1110 (224) as its most significant nibble, and the channel number value as the least significant nibble. Two data bytes are used, and the two seven bit values these contain are combined to give a 14 bit pitch wheel value. The least significant byte is the one sent first. A value of 10000000000000 (8192) represents zero pitch change. If less than the full 14 bit resolution is implemented some of the least significant bits are ignored by a receiving device, and always set at zero by a transmitting device.

Programme Change

The programme change code nibble is 1100 (192). The least significant nibble of the header byte is the channel number value. The header is followed by a single data byte, which is the number of the new programme for that channel. The value in the data byte is from 0 to 127, but some manufacturers number programmes differently. Where this is the case, equipment manuals often have a conversion chart to make things easier.

This table provides a summary of the channel messages for quick reference purposes. The channel mode messages require some further amplification, and this is provided in the next table.

Header	Function	Data
1000 (128)	Note Off	Note Value/Velocity Value
1001 (144)	Note On	Note Value/Velocity Value

216

1010 (160)	Poly Key Pressure	Note Value/Pressure Value
1011 (176)	Control Change	Control Number/Value
1100 (192)	Programme Change	New Programme Number
1101 (208)	Overall Pressure	Pressure Value
1110 (224)	Pitch Wheel	l.s.b./m.s.b.

Control No.	Function	Data
121	Reset All Controls	0
122	Local Control	0 = off, 127 = on
123	All Notes Off	0
124	Omni Mode Off	0
125	Omni Mode On	0
126	Mono Mode On	Number Of Channels (0 = All Channels Set To Mono Mode)
127	Poly Mode On	0

System Messages

These all have 1111 as the most significant nibble in the header byte. No channel numbers are used, as these messages are sent to the whole system. This leaves the least significant nibble free to indicate the type of system message. The next table gives a full list of these messages, but note that some of the sixteen available codes are as yet undefined. Many of them do not require data bytes, and are just single byte messages.

Nibble Code	Function	Data
0000 (0)	System Exclusive	ID/As Required
0001 (1)	MTC Quarter Frame	Frame ID and Value
0010 (2)	Song Position Pointer	l.s.b./m.s.b.
0011 (3)	Song Select	Song Number
0100 (4)	Undefined	
0101 (5)	Undefined	
0110 (6)	Tune Request	None
0111 (7)	End System Exclusive	None
1000 (8)	Clock Signal	None
1001 (9)	Undefined	
1010 (10)	Start	None
1011 (11)	Continue	None
1100 (12)	Stop	None

217

1101 (13)	Undefined	
1110 (14)	Active Sensing	None
1111 (15)	System Reset	None

The values shown in brackets are the decimal equivalents for the binary nibbles. These must be boosted by 240 to give the total decimal value for each header byte (e.g. the value sent for a clock signal is $240 + 8 = 248$). The system exclusive message is followed by a data byte which gives the manufacturer's identification code, and then as many data bytes as required follow on from this. The "end system exclusive" message marks the end of a system exclusive message. The next table provides a partial list of manufacturer's identification numbers. The sample dump standard is a "system exclusive common" message, which can be used by any MIDI equipment producer. There are now so many ID numbers that there are not enough single byte codes to accommodate them all. Consequently, some ID numbers are now three bytes long.

Manufacturer	*Number (decimal)*
SC1	1
Big Briar	2
Octave	3
Moog	4
Passport Designs	5
Lexicon	6
Ensonique	15
Oberheim	16
Apple Computer	17
Emu Systems	24
Eventide	28
Clarity	31
Passac	32
SIEL	33
PPG	41
JEN	42
Elka	47
Dynacord	48
Soundcraft Electronics	57

Kawai	64
Roland	65
Korg	66
Yamaha	67
Casio	68
Akai	71
Sony	76
TEAC	78
Matsushita Electric	80
Fostex	81
Sample Dump Standard	126
Alesis	0 0 14
Opcode	0 0 22
Orban	0 0 33
Musonix	0 0 100

General MIDI

General MIDI system, level 1 (better known as just "General MIDI" or "GM"), is a specification for a MIDI system that can be used to play standard sequencer files, giving fully predictable results. It includes a full set of sound assignments for program numbers. This enables the correct sound for each channel to be selected using a series of program change messages at the beginning of each sequence. Channel 10 is used exclusively for non-melodic percussion sounds (i.e. percussion sounds of fixed pitch), and has a separate set of sound assignments. This is a full list of the channel 10 assignments. It is followed by details of the group and individual assignments for the other 15 channels.

Program No.	*Percussion Sound*
35	Acoustic Bass Drum
36	Bass Drum 1
37	Side Stick
38	Acoustic Snare
39	Hand Clap
40	Electric Snare
41	Low Floor Tom
42	Closed Hi-Hat
43	High Floor Tom

44	Pedal Hi-Hat
45	Low Tom
46	Open Hi-Hat
47	Low Mid Tom
48	High Mid Tom
49	Crash Cymbal 1
50	High Tom
51	Ride Cymbal 1
52	Chinese Cymbal
53	Ride Bell
54	Tambourine
55	Splash Cymbal
56	Cowbell
57	Crash Cymbal 2
58	Vibraslap
59	Ride Cymbal 2
60	High Bongo
61	Low Bongo
62	Mute Hi Conga
63	Open Hi Conga
64	Low Conga
65	High Timbale
66	Low Timbale
67	High Agogo
68	Low Agogo 2
69	Cabasa
70	Maracas
71	Short Whistle
72	Long Whistle
73	Short Guiro
74	Long Guiro
75	Claves
76	High Woodblock
77	Low Woodblock
78	Mute Cuica
79	Open Cuica
80	Mute Triangle
81	Open Triangle

General MIDI Sound Assignment Groups (not channel 10)

Program No.	Group
1 - 8	Piano
9 - 16	Chromatic Percussion
17 - 24	Organ
25 - 32	Guitar
33 - 40	Bass
41 - 48	Strings
49 - 56	Ensemble
57 - 64	Brass
65 - 72	Reed
73 - 80	Pipe
81 - 88	Synth Lead
89 - 96	Synth Pad
97 - 104	Synth Effects
105 - 112	Ethnic
113 - 120	Percussive
121 - 128	Sound Effects

Melodic Instrument Sound Assignments

Program No.	Instrument
1	Grand Piano
2	Bright Acoustic Piano
3	Electric Grand Piano
4	Honky-Tonk Piano
5	Electric Piano 1
6	Electric Piano 2
7	Harpsichord
8	Clavi
9	Celesta
10	Glockenspiel
11	Music Box
12	Vibraphone
13	Marimba
14	Xylophone
15	Tubular Bells

16	Dulcimer
17	Drawbar Organ
18	Percussive Organ
19	Rock Organ
20	Church Organ
21	Reed Organ
22	Accordion
23	Harmonica
24	Tango Accordion
25	Acoustic Guitar (nylon strings)
26	Acoustic Guitar (steel strings)
27	Electric Guitar (jazz)
28	Electric Guitar (clean)
29	Electric Guitar (muted)
30	Overdriven Guitar
31	Distortion Guitar
32	Guitar Harmonics
33	Acoustic Bass
34	Electric Bass (finger)
35	Electric Bass (pick)
36	Fretless Bass
37	Slap Bass 1
38	Slap Bass 2
39	Synth Bass 1
40	Synth Bass 2
41	Violin
42	Viola
43	Cello
44	Contrabass
45	Tremolo Strings
46	Pizzicato Strings
47	Orchestral Harp
48	Timpani
49	String Ensemble 1
50	String Ensemble 2

51	Synth Strings 1
52	Synth Strings 2
53	Choir Aahs
54	Voice Ooohs
55	Synth Voice
56	Orchestra Hit
57	Trumpet
58	Trombone
59	Tuba
60	Muted Trumpet
61	French Horn
62	Brass Section
63	Synth Brass 1
64	Synth Brass 2
65	Soprano Sax
66	Alto Sax
67	Tenor Sax
68	Baritone Sax
69	Oboe
70	English Horn
71	Bassoon
72	Clarinet
73	Piccolo
74	Flute
75	Recorder
76	Pan Flute
77	Blown Bottle
78	Shakuhachi
79	Whistle
80	Ocarina
81	Lead 1 (square)
82	Lead 2 (sawtooth)
83	Lead 3 (calliope)
84	Lead 4 (chiff)
85	Lead 5 (charang)
86	Lead 6 (voice)

87	Lead 7 (fifths)
88	Lead 8 (bass & lead)
89	Pad 1 (new age)
90	Pad 2 (warm)
91	Pad 3 (polysynth)
92	Pad 4 (choir)
93	Pad 5 (bowed)
94	Pad 6 (metallic)
95	Pad 7 (halo)
96	Pad 8 (sweep)
97	FX 1 (rain)
98	FX 2 (soundtrack)
99	FX 3 (crystal)
100	FX 4 (atmosphere)
101	FX 5 (brightness)
102	FX 6 (goblins)
103	FX 7 (echoes)
104	FX 8 (sci-fi)
105	Sitar
106	Banjo
107	Shamisen
108	Koto
109	Kalimba
110	Bagpipe
111	Fiddle
112	Shanai
113	Tinkle Bell
114	Agogo
115	Steel Drums
116	Woodblock
117	Taiko Drum
118	Melodic Tom
119	Synth Drum
120	Reverse Cymbal
121	Guitar Fret Noise

122	Breath Noise
123	Seashore
124	Bird Tweet
125	Telephone Ring
126	Helicopter
127	Applause
128	Gunshot

Circuit Symbols

Figures 6.2 to 6.4 show a range of circuit symbols. I would not claim that every circuit symbol is included in these diagrams, but the vast majority of circuit symbols that you will ever encounter are provided here. Note that these diagrams do not include the logic and amplifier circuit symbols that have been covered in previous chapters. Note also, that the circuit symbol for an integrated circuit, other than an amplifier or certain logic types, is simply a rectangle.

When dealing with circuit symbols you should always bear in mind that there are differences in drawing style from one circuit diagram to the next. Another point to keep in mind is that some symbols have changed over the years. Some of the old versions are still much used today. The best example of this is the zig-zag resistor symbol, which is used by many electronics magazines, etc., despite the fact that the box style resistor symbol is the current British standard. The zig-zag version is included in the diagrams, but the variations on this symbol (potentiometer, preset, etc.) are not. These are basically the same as their box style equivalents, but with the zig-zag in place of the box. Apart from the various types of resistor, where appropriate, the diagrams show both the old and new versions of circuit symbols.

You may occasionally encounter circuit diagrams where all two-terminal components are simply represented by small rectangles, like the box style resistor symbol. This method was never generally adopted in the U.K., but plenty of circuits of this type can be found in service manuals for equipment manufactured outside the U.K. Circuit diagrams of this type tend to be unpopular with the people who have to use them, because the only way of telling the type of component represented by a particular box is to read the component number beside it (C1 is

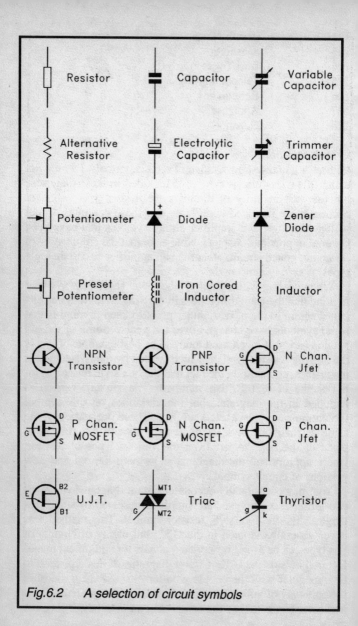

Fig.6.2   A selection of circuit symbols

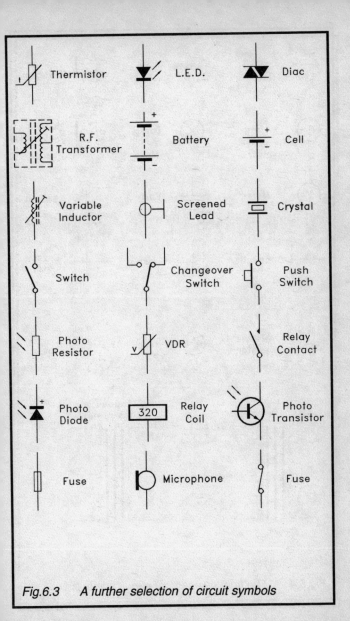

Fig.6.3   A further selection of circuit symbols

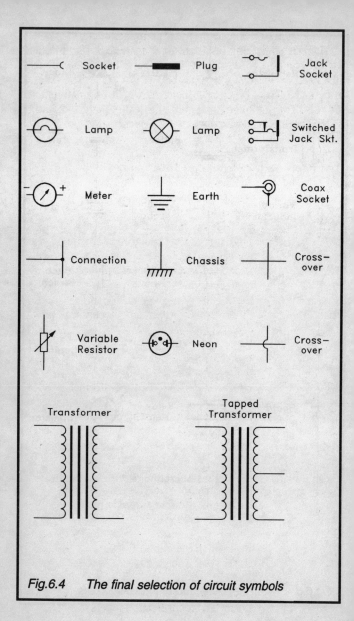

Fig.6.4   The final selection of circuit symbols

228

a capacitor, R10 is a resistor, L2 is an inductor, etc.).

There is something less than total agreement on the letters used in component identification numbers. Transistors are usually "TR" in the U.K., but can be "Tr" or "Q". The latter is often to be found on circuit diagrams which originate outside the U.K. This list of component identification letters should be useful for reference purposes.

Letter(s)	Component
B	Battery
BY	Battery
C	Capacitor (any fixed value type)
CH	Chassis
CRT	Cathode ray tube
CSR	Thyristor or triac (controlled silicon rectifier)
D	Diode (any type, including photodiodes, l.e.d.s, and rectifiers)
E	Earth
FL	Filter (usually a ceramic, mechanical, or crystal type)
FS	Fuse
JK	Jack socket
IC	Integrated circuit
IFT	Intermediate frequency transformer
L	Inductor
LP	Lamp (neon or filament, but not a l.e.d.)
LS	Loudspeaker
M	Motor
ME	Meter
Mic	Microphone
PCC	Photo conductive cell (photo-resistor, usually a cadmium sulphide type)
PL	Plug (any type)
Q	Transistor
R	Resistor (fixed value)
RL	Relay (coil or contacts)
S	Switch
SK	Socket (any type, but jack sockets are often given 'JK' identification letters)

SW	Switch
T	Transformer (any type including r.f.)
TC	Trimmer capacitor (preset variable capacitor)
Th	Thermistor
TL	Earphone or headphones
Tr	Transistor
TR	Transistor
V	Valve (any type except c.r.t.)
VC	Variable capacitor
VR	Variable resistor or potentiometer
WD	Warning device (horn, bell, buzzer, etc.)
X	Crystal

On bipolar transistor circuit symbols the letters "e", "b", and "c" are sometimes used to respectively indicate the emitter, base, and collector terminals. For field effect transistors the corresponding letters are "s", "g", and "d", indicating the source, gate, and drain terminals respectively.

Centronics Interface

Most computers and printers are equipped with a Centronics style parallel interface. A parallel interface sends data in complete bytes over eight lines plus an earth line, permitting a very high rate of transfer. In fact rates of 500k per second or more can be achieved, but the maximum cable length is quite limited. The maximum recommended cable length for a parallel printer connection is just two metres, although somewhat longer cables are usually satisfactory in practice. In addition to the data lines there are various handshake lines which regulate the flow of data from the computer to the printer. A parallel printer interface provides only one-way communication, apart from status information sent from the printer to the computer via the handshake lines. There are numerous earth connections. When a ribbon cable is used, these connect to leads that provide screening between one data line and the next, and between handshake lines.

Figure 6.5 shows the pin numbering for a standard Centronics input (i.e. the port on the printer). This shows the port as viewed from outside the printer. The connector is a 36

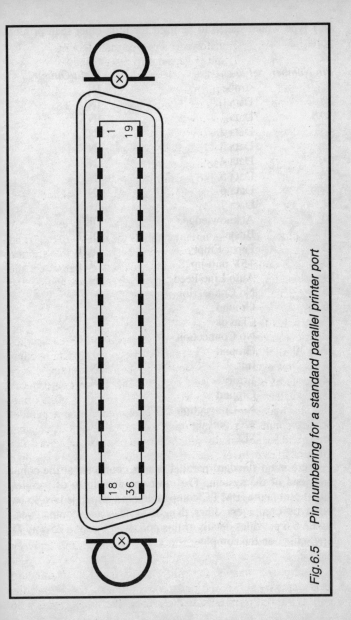

Fig. 6.5   Pin numbering for a standard parallel printer port

way type which seems to be used for little other than printer ports.

Pin Number	Function	Input/Output
1	strobe	IN
2	Data 0	IN
3	Data 1	IN
4	Data 2	IN
5	Data 3	IN
6	Data 4	IN
7	Data 5	IN
8	Data 6	IN
9	Data 7	IN
10	Acknowledge	OUT
11	Busy	OUT
12	Paper Empty	OUT
13	+5V pull-up	OUT
14	Auto Line Feed	IN
15	No Connection	–
16	Ground	–
17	Chassis	–
18	No Connection	–
19 to 30	Ground	–
31	Init.	IN
32	Error	OUT
33	Ground	–
34	No Connection	–
35	+5V pull-up	OUT
36	SLCT	IN

There is no standard parallel printer connector at the computer end of the system. The most common form of parallel output port is the IBM PC compatible type, which is now to be found on computers other than IBM PCs and compatibles. Figure 6.6 provides details of this port, which uses a 25 way D type socket on the computer.

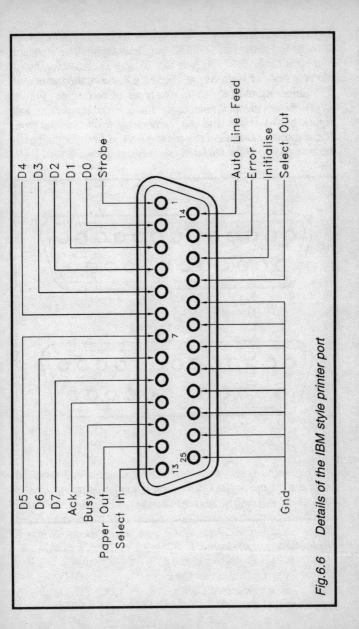

Fig.6.6   Details of the IBM style printer port

RS232C Interface

This list is for the full RS232C implementation. The standard connector for an RS232C port is a 25 way D connector, but it can be a male or female type. Figure 6.7 shows the method of pin numbering used for these two types of connector. Figure 6.7(a) shows the pin numbering for a male connector, and Figure 6.7(b) shows the pin numbering for a female type. These show rear views of the connectors (i.e. seen looking onto the pins to which the soldered connections are made).

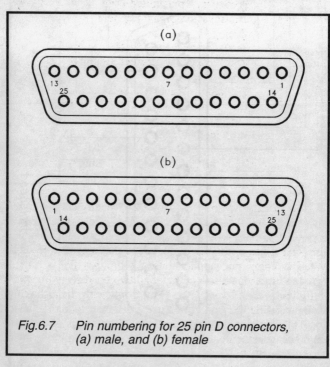

Fig.6.7   Pin numbering for 25 pin D connectors, (a) male, and (b) female

Pin Number	Function	Input/Output
1	Protective Ground	–
2	Transmitted Data	OUT
3	Received Data	IN
4	Request To Send (RTS)	OUT

5	Clear To Send (CTS)	IN
6	Data Set Ready (DSR)	IN
7	Signal Ground	–
8	Data Carrier Detect (DCD)	IN
9	Reserved For Data Set Testing	–
10	Reserved For Data Set Testing	–
11	Not Used	–
12	Sec. Rec. Line Sig. Det.	–
13	Secondary CTS	–
14	Secondary Transmitted Data	–
15	Transmission Signal Element Timing	–
16	Secondary Received Data	–
17	Receiver Signal Element Timing	–
18	Not Used	–
19	Secondary Request To Send	–
20	Data Terminal Ready (DTR)	OUT
21	Signal Quality Detector	–
22	Ring Indicator	IN
23	Data Signal Rate Selector	–
24	Transmit Signal Element Timing	–
25	Not Used	–

Note that many serial ports are substantially cut down versions of the full system. The RS232C interface was designed as a general purpose type not intended specifically for computer use, and it has a number of functions that are of little or no value in computing applications. As little as five terminals (ground, data input, data output, and two handshake lines) are sufficient for a basic two way link with handshaking. Computer RS232C ports often use a different type of connector. This is understandable, since the 25 terminals of the standard D connector are unnecessary with perhaps only five or six terminals actually being implemented. On the other hand, it does mean that standard RS232C connecting leads are unusable with these ports (although ready-made serial leads for many non-standard ports are available). Figure 6.8 provides details of the nine pin "AT" style RS232C port used on many PCs. The connector on the computer is a nine way D type plug.

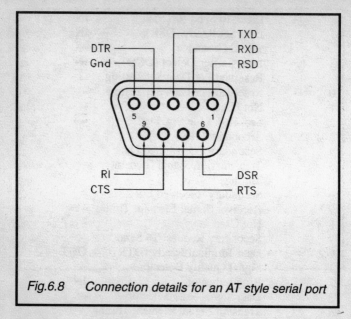

Fig.6.8   Connection details for an AT style serial port

Parallel R - Series C

The formula for calculating parallel resistance (Figure 6.9(a)) is:

$$R\ total = (R1 \times R2)/(R1 + R2)$$

For example, suppose that the values of R1 and R2 are 10k and 33k. This works out at 330/43, which equals 7.674k. The formula for calculating series capacitance is essentially the same:

$$C\ total = (C1 \times C2)/(C1 + C2)$$

As a simple example, suppose that C1 and C2 have values of 4n7 and 15n. This works out at 70.5/19.7, which gives a final answer of 3.579n.

Calculating parallel capacitance (Figure 6.10(a)) and series resistance (Figure 6.10(b)) is very simple. It is just a matter of adding the values of the two components. For instance, if C1 and C2 have values of 10n and 68n, their total capacitance in parallel is 78n.

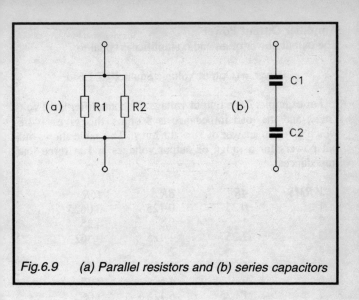

Fig.6.9   (a) Parallel resistors and (b) series capacitors

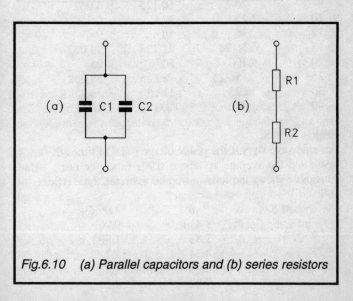

Fig.6.10   (a) Parallel capacitors and (b) series resistors

Amplifier Output Power

The output power of an audio amplifier is equal to:

$$\text{Power} = \text{(Output Voltage Squared)}/Z \text{ Load}$$

For example, if the output voltage of an amplifier is 12 volts r.m.s., and the load impedance is 8 ohms, this gives 144/8, which gives an answer of 18 watts r.m.s. This table shows output powers for a range of output voltages and at three load impedances.

V RMS	4R	8R	16R
1	0.25	0.125	0.0625
2	1	0.5	0.25
3	2.25	1.125	0.562
4	4	2	1
5	6.25	3.125	1.562
6	9	4.5	2.25
7	12.25	6.125	3.062
8	16	8	4
9	20.25	10.125	5.062
10	25	12.5	6.25
12	36	18	9
15	56.25	28.125	14.062
20	100	50	25
25	156.25	78.125	39.062
30	225	112.5	56.25
40	400	200	100

Peak – R.M.S.

For sinewave signals the peak voltage is 1.414 times the r.m.s. level, and the average voltage is 0.901 times the r.m.s. value. This table shows the relationship between the three types.

R.M.S.	Peak	Average
1	1.414	0.901
2	2.83	1.802
3	4.24	2.7
4	5.66	3.6
5	7.07	4.51

6	8.48	5.41
7	9.90	6.31
8	11.3	7.21
9	12.7	8.11
10	14.1	9.01

Decibel Ratios

Decibels are a means of expressing power ratios, but they are also used to express voltage ratios. The scaling is logarithmic, which gives good accuracy with small ratios, but also enables very high ratios to be expressed without resorting to numbers umpteen digits long. This table shows the relationship between a range of decibel values and their power/voltage ratios.

dB	Power Ratio	Voltage Ratio
0	1	1
0.5	1.122	1.059
1	1.259	1.122
1.5	1.413	1.189
2	1.585	1.259
2.5	1.778	1.334
3	1.995	1.413
3.5	2.239	1.496
4	2.512	1.585
4.5	2.818	1.679
5	3.162	1.778
6	3.981	1.995
7	5.012	2.239
8	6.31	2.512
9	7.943	2.818
10	10	3.162
11	12.59	3.548
12	15.85	3.981
13	19.95	4.467
14	25.12	5.012
15	31.62	5.623
16	39.81	6.31
17	50.12	7.079
18	63.1	7.943
19	79.43	8.913

20	100	10
30	1,000	31.62
40	10,000	100
50	100,000	316.2
60	1,000,000	1,000
70	10,000,000	3,162
80	100,000,000	10,000
90	1,000,000,000	31,620
100	10,000,000,000	100,000

Please note following is a list of other titles that are available in our range of Radio, Electronics and Computer books.

These should be available from all good Booksellers, Radio Component Dealers and Mail Order Companies.

However, should you experience difficulty in obtaining any title in your area, then please write directly to the Publisher enclosing payment to cover the cost of the book plus adequate postage.

If you would like a complete catalogue of our entire range of Radio, Electronics and Computer books, then please send a Stamped Addressed Envelope to:

BERNARD BABANI (publishing) LTD
THE GRAMPIANS
SHEPHERDS BUSH ROAD
LONDON W6 7NF
ENGLAND

160	Coil Design and Construction Manual	£2.50
227	Beginners Guide to Building Electronic Projects	£1.95
BP28	Resistor Selection Handbook	£0.60
BP36	50 Circuits Using Germanium Silicon & Zener Diodes	£1.95
BP37	50 Projects Using Relays, SCRs and TRIACs	£2.95
BP39	50 (FET) Field Effect Transistor Projects	£2.95
BP42	50 Simple LED Circuits	£1.95
BP44	IC 555 Projects	£2.95
BP48	Electronic Projects for Beginners	£1.95
BP49	Popular Electronic Projects	£2.50
BP53	Practical Electronics Calculations & Formulae	£3.95
BP56	Electronic Security Devices	£2.95
BP74	Electronic Music Projects	£2.95
BP76	Power Supply Projects	£2.50
BP78	Practical Computer Experiments	£1.75
BP80	Popular Electronic Circuits – Book 1	£2.95
BP84	Digital IC Projects	£1.95
BP85	International Transistor Equivalents Guide	£3.95
BP87	50 Simple LED Circuits – Book 2	£1.95
BP88	How to Use Op-amps	£2.95
BP90	Audio Projects	£2.50
BP92	Electronics Simplified – Crystal Set Construction	£1.75
BP94	Electronic Projects for Cars and Boats	£1.95
BP95	Model Railway Projects	£2.95
BP97	IC Projects for Beginners	£1.95
BP98	Popular Electronic Circuits – Book 2	£2.95
BP99	Mini-matrix Board Projects	£2.50
BP105	Aerial Projects	£2.50
BP107	30 Solderless Breadboard Projects – Book 1	£2.95
BP110	How to Get Your Electronic Projects Working	£2.95
BP111	Audio	£3.95
BP115	The Pre-computer Book	£1.95
BP118	Practical Electronic Building Blocks – Book 2	£1.95
BP121	How to Design and Make Your Own PCB's	£2.50
BP122	Audio Amplifier Construction	£2.95
BP125	25 Simple Amateur Band Aerials	£1.95
BP126	BASIC & PASCAL in Parallel	£1.50
BP130	Micro Interfacing Circuits – Book 1	£2.75
BP131	Micro Interfacing Circuits – Book 2	£2.75
BP132	25 Simple SW Broadcast Band Aerials	£1.95
BP136	25 Simple Indoor and Window Aerials	£1.75
BP137	BASIC & FORTRAN in Parallel	£1.95
BP138	BASIC & FORTH in Parallel	£1.95
BP144	Further Practical Electronics Calculations & Formulae	£4.95
BP145	25 Simple Tropical and MW Band Aerials	£1.75
BP146	The Pre-BASIC Book	£2.95
BP147	An Introduction to 6502 Machine Code	£2.95
BP148	Computer Terminology Explained	£1.95
BP171	Easy Add-on Projects for Amstrad CPC 464, 664, 6128 & MSX Computers	£2.95
BP176	A TV-DXers Handbook (Revised Edition)	£5.95
BP177	An Introduction to Computer Communications	£2.95
BP179	Electronic Circuits for the Computer Control of Robots	£2.95
BP182	MIDI Projects	£2.95
BP184	An Introduction to 68000 Assembly Language	£2.95
BP187	A Practical Reference Guide to Word Processing on the Amstrad PCW8256 & PCW8512	£5.95
BP190	More Advanced Electronic Security Projects	£2.95
BP192	More Advanced Power Supply Projects	£2.95
BP193	LOGO for Beginners	£2.95
BP196	BASIC & LOGO in Parallel	£2.95
BP197	An Introduction to the Amstrad PC's	£5.95
BP198	An Introduction to Antenna Theory	£2.95
BP230	A Concise Introduction to GEM	£2.95
BP232	A Concise Introduction to MS-DOS	£2.95
BP233	Electronic Hobbyists Handbook	£4.95
BP239	Getting the Most From Your Multimeter	£2.95
BP240	Remote Control Handbook	£3.95
BP243	BBC BASIC86 on the Amstrad PC's & IBM Compatibles – Book 1: Language	£3.95
BP244	BBC BASIC86 on the Amstrad PC's & IBM Compatibles – Book 2: Graphics and Disk Files	£3.95
BP245	Digital Audio Projects	£2.95
BP246	Musical Applications of the Atari ST's	£5.95
BP247	More Advanced MIDI Projects	£2.95
BP248	Test Equipment Construction	£2.95
BP249	More Advanced Test Equipment Construction	£3.50
BP250	Programming in FORTRAN 77	£4.95
BP251	Computer Hobbyists Handbook	£5.95
BP254	From Atoms to Amperes	£3.50
BP255	International Radio Stations Guide (Revised 1991/92 Edition)	£5.95
BP256	An Introduction to Loudspeakers & Enclosure Design	£2.95
BP257	An Introduction to Amateur Radio	£3.50
BP258	Learning to Program in C (Revised Edition)	£4.95
BP259	A Concise Introduction to UNIX	£2.95
BP260	A Concise Introduction to OS/2	£2.95
BP261	A Concise Introduction to Lotus 1-2-3 (Revised Edition)	£3.95

BP262	A Concise Introduction to Wordperfect (Revised Edition)	£3.95
BP264	A Concise Advanced User's Guide to MS-DOS (Revised Edition)	£3.95
BP265	More Advanced Uses of the Multimeter	£2.95
BP266	Electronic Modules and Systems for Beginners	£3.95
BP267	How to Use Oscilloscopes & Other Test Equipment	£3.50
BP269	An Introduction to Desktop Publishing	£5.95
BP270	A Concise Introduction to Symphony	£3.95
BP271	How to Expand, Modernise & Repair PC's & Compatibles	£4.95
BP272	Interfacing PC's and Compatibles	£3.95
BP273	Practical Electronic Sensors	£4.95
BP274	A Concise Introduction to SuperCalc5	£3.95
BP275	Simple Short Wave Receiver Construction	£3.95
BP276	Short Wave Superhet Receiver Construction	£2.95
BP277	High Power Audio Amplifier Construction	£3.95
BP278	Experimental Antenna Topics	£3.50
BP279	A Concise Introduction to Excel	£3.95
BP280	Getting the Most From Your PC's Hard Disk	£3.95
BP281	An Introduction to VHF/UHF for Radio Amateurs	£3.50
BP282	Understanding PC Specifications	£3.95
BP283	A Concise Introduction to SmartWare II	£4.95
BP284	Programming in QuickBASIC	£4.95
BP285	A Beginners Guide to Modern Electronic Components	£3.95
BP286	A Reference Guide to Basic Electronics Terms	£5.95
BP287	A Reference Guide to Practical Electronics Terms	£5.95
BP288	A Concise Introduction to Windows3.0	£3.95
BP290	An Introduction to Amateur Communications Satellite	£3.95
BP291	A Concise Introduction to Ventura	£3.95
BP292	Public Address Loudspeaker Systems	£3.95
BP293	An Introduction to Radio Wave Propagation	£3.95
BP294	A Concise Introduction to Microsoft Works	£4.95
BP295	A Concise Introduction to Word for Windows	£4.95
BP297	Loudspeakers for Musicians	£3.95
BP298	A Concise Introduction to the Mac System & Finder	£3.95
BP299	Practical Electronic Filters	£4.95
BP300	Setting Up An Amateur Radio Station	£3.95
BP301	Antennas for VHF and UHF	£3.95
BP302	A Concise Users Guide to Lotus 1-2-3 Release 3.1	£3.95
BP303	Understanding PC Software	£4.95
BP304	Projects for Radio Amateurs and SWLs	£3.95
BP305	Learning CAD with AutoSketch for Windows	£5.95
BP306	A Concise Introduction to Ami Pro 3	£4.95
BP307	A Concise Introduction to QuarkXPress	£4.95
BP308	A Concise Introduction to Word 5.1 on the Macintosh	£5.95
BP309	Preamplifier and Filter Circuits	£3.95
BP310	Acoustic Feedback – How to Avoid It	£3.95
BP311	An Introduction to Scanners and Scanning	£4.95
BP312	An Introduction to Microwaves	£3.95
BP313	A Concise Introduction to Sage	£3.95
BP314	A Concise Introduction to Quattro Pro	£4.95
BP315	An Introduction to the Electromagnetic Wave	£4.95
BP316	Practical Electronic Design Data	£4.95
BP317	Practical Electronic Timing	£4.95
BP318	A Concise User's Guide to MS-DOS 5	£4.95
BP319	Making MS-DOS Work for You	£4.95
BP320	Electronic Projects for Your PC	£3.95
BP321	Circuit Source – Book 1	£4.95
BP322	Circuit Source – Book 2	£4.95
BP323	How to Choose a Small Business Computer System	£4.95
BP324	The Art of Soldering	£3.95
BP325	A Concise Users Guide to Windows3.1	£4.95
BP326	The Electronics of Satellite Communications	£4.95
BP327	MS-DOS One Step at a Time	£4.95
BP328	Sage Explained	£5.95
BP329	Electronic Music Learning Projects	£4.95
BP330	A Concise User's Guide to Lotus 1-2-3 Release 2.4	£4.95
BP331	A Beginners Guide to MIDI	£4.95
BP332	A Beginners Guide to TTL Digital ICs	£4.95
BP333	A Beginners Guide to CMOS Digital ICs	£4.95
BP334	Magic Electronic Projects	£4.95
BP335	Operational Amplifier User's Handbook	£5.95
BP336	A Concise User's Guide to Lotus 1-2-3 Release 3.4	£5.95
BP337	A Concise Users Guide to Lotus 1-2-3 for Windows	£5.95
BP338	A Concise Introduction to Word for Windows	£5.95
BP339	A Concise Introduction to Wordperfect 5.2 for Windows	£5.95
BP340	A Concise Introduction to dBase V	£4.95
BP341	A Concise Users Guide to MS-DOS 6	£5.95
BP342	A Conciser Users Guide to Lotus Improv	£5.95